CH

John S. Clarke

TEACH YOURSELF BOOKS
Hodder and Stoughton

First published 1988
Second impression 1989

Copyright © 1988
J. S. Clarke

No part of this publication may be reproduced or
transmitted in any form or by any means, electronically or
mechanically, including photocopying, recording or any
information storage or retrieval system, without either the
prior permission in writing from the publisher or a licence,
permitting restricted copying, issued by the Copyright
Licensing Agency, 33–34 Alfred Place,
London WC1E 7DP.

British Library Cataloguing in Publication Data
Clarke, J. S. (John Shipley), *1933–*
Teach yourself chemistry.
1. Chemistry
I. Title
540

ISBN 0 340 42871 6

Printed and bound in Great Britain for
Hodder and Stoughton Educational,
a division of Hodder and Stoughton Ltd,
Mill Road, Dunton Green, Sevenoaks, Kent TN13 2YD,
by Richard Clay Ltd, Bungay, Suffolk.
Photoset by Rowland Phototypesetting Ltd,
Bury St Edmunds, Suffolk.

Contents

Acknowledgments

The publishers would like to thank the following for their kind permission to reproduce copyright photographs:

Department of the Environment, p5; Barnaby's Picture Library, p7; Thames Water Authority, p8; CEGB, p11; British Geological Survey, p19; Shell, p20; CEGB, pp33,37; UKAEA, p38; Royal Astronomical Society, p39; Cambridge Scientific Instruments Ltd/Dr R Blaschke Munster, p60; The Science Museum, p66; David Lee Photography Ltd., p70; Fisons Scientific Equipment, p76; Rolls-Royce, p87; Blue Circle Industries PLC, p109; Tony O'Malley Pictures Ltd., p127; ICI, p130; Chubb Fire Security Ltd., p132; The Scotch Whisky Association/Anthony James, p140.

Introduction

All syllabuses for chemistry at 16+ have been re-written with the introduction of the General Certificate of Secondary Education. New text books must emphasise the social, economic, environmental and technological aspects of chemistry. They must not do this to the exclusion of experimental fact or theory because what is important one year may not be considered so next year. Chemistry affects our day-to-day lives in more ways than many people realise. The chemical industry supplies many of the things we need or want and does so directly and indirectly. The chemical industry is one of our most important wealth-producing industries. The environmental consequences of our way of life cannot be avoided. Whether we consider fertilisers, cars, aspirins, alcohol or food there are advantages and disadvantages of manufacture and use to be faced.

The first part of the book (Chapters 1–7) looks at our resources. The second part (Chapters 8–13) considers pure substances and is extended to a preliminary division of elements into metals and non-metals. The third part (Chapters 14–20) discusses the making, the properties and the uses of elements and compounds. Part four (Chapters 21–27), the classification of substances and changes, develops some of the underlying patterns that may have become apparent. This leads on to the fifth part (Chapters 28–32) which looks at the importance of the structure of the atom and the bonding of atoms in elements and compounds. The last part deals with measuring quantities of substances and concludes with a summary of useful analytical information. Scattered in the text are a few questions for you to answer. You may choose to read the chapters in a different order but I hope that there are sufficient cross-references to assist you to understand the subject.

The main requirements of all GCSE syllabuses have been covered. Within the space of this book it is not possible to deal adequately with some minor points. The language has been kept as simple as possible without doing injustice to the subject. Every opportunity has been taken to use examples relevant to everyday life.

It is a pleasure to acknowledge the considerable help given by my wife and son who, together with a selection of pupils from Alleyn's School, have done their best on your behalf to ask the questions that you would like answered. I am also grateful to the industries and public bodies who have answered my questions and sent me photographs to illustrate the text.

J.S.C.

Chemistry and You

Chemistry for you

Air, water, food, fuel and clothing; what is vital and what is not? You breathe in air, sometimes quickly, sometimes slowly: it depends on what you are doing. Air is a mixture of oxygen, nitrogen and some other gases. You cannot do without the oxygen in the air for more than a few minutes or you would die. You have a drink every few hours. You could not do without water for more than a few days, even if it is flavoured with fruit squash, tea or coffee. You breathe out the air and some of the waste products you don't want. You go to the toilet to excrete other waste products.

If you eat meals regularly you are lucky compared to many people in the world. You could live without food for a few weeks but you probably don't want to try. For breakfast you might put common salt (sodium chloride) on an egg, spread margarine on your toast and put milk in your tea. The food is broken down into smaller parts as it travels through your body. This happens with the help of catalysts in your saliva and the hydrochloric acid in your stomach. Some of the food dissolves in your blood and is stored if it is not used immediately. Many of the parts of the food you have eaten react with the oxygen taken out of the air by your blood. Food is a biological fuel and gives you energy to live and work. You are a chemical reaction on two legs!

In winter you burn fuels such as natural gas (methane) to keep yourself warm. To travel around you use other fuels such as petrol and diesel oil. Your transport is probably made of metals such as steel or aluminium, with parts made of glass, plastics and rubber.

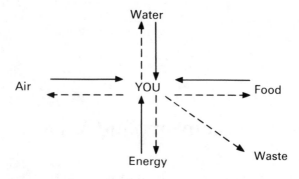

Fig. 1.   You are a chemical reaction on two legs

Again, the oxygen of the air is vital for the fuel to burn and there are waste products in the exhaust gases. Some vehicles have electric motors: electricity is mostly made by the combustion of coal. A few vehicles run on motors using batteries in which chemical reactions make electricity.

You keep warm by wearing clothing. Once upon a time clothing was nearly always made from wool or cotton. Today most clothing is made from nylon, rayon, Acrilan or polyester (Terylene) which are all synthetic.

Chemistry in action

The quality of the air you breathe is checked, especially if you work in industry. Many gases are safe in small proportions but even oxygen would not be good for you if you breathed it pure and undiluted for a long time. You may live in a smokefree zone, a consequence of the Clean Air Act.

If you drank fresh rainwater you might not get some of the minerals you need in order to grow and live a healthy life. River and lake water must be sterilised so that the water is fit to drink. The germs in water are killed by using chlorine or ozone.

When you wash you use water and soap. Soap is a detergent, a cleaning agent. It is made from animal fat by boiling it with sodium hydroxide solution (an alkali). Soapless detergents, often just called detergents, are made from oil with sulphuric acid and then sodium hydroxide.

Farmers need synthetic (man-made) fertilisers, such as ammonium nitrate, because natural fertilisers are not plentiful enough. This fertiliser is made by industry from air, water and natural gas. The farmer may grow wheat which can be ground into flour. Flour is made into bread and then you can make toast. The cows in the farmer's fields eat green grass but give you white milk. What complex chemical reactions must occur inside the cows! You cannot eat grass but you can eat the meat of a cow or drink its milk. Milk can be made into butter and part of it (whey) is used to make margarine.

Crude oil (petroleum) is found under the North Sea and in many other parts of the world. Chemists separate this mixture into bottled gases for camping, petrol, diesel fuel, lubricating oil and bitumen. Some parts of the oil are used to make plastics and synthetic rubber.

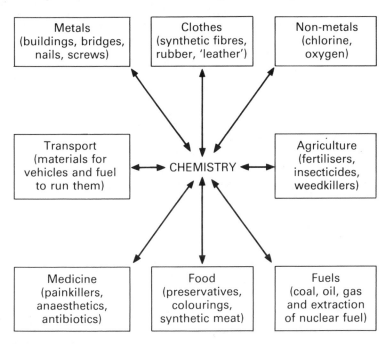

Fig. 2. A few of the areas where chemistry is in action. Don't forget paints, plastics, perfumes, detergents and cooking ('applied' chemistry). Can you list some more?

Some of the products are burnt to give energy. The supply of fuels in the world may be running out. Oil, coal and natural gas are fossil fuels because they were made millions of years ago from the remains of plants and animals.

The synthetic fibres used for your clothing are made from oil by the chemical industry. These synthetic fibres shrink less than natural fibres if they get wet and it is easier to put a permanent crease in them if needed. The supply of natural fibres is not sufficient. If we had to use more land to grow cotton and to rear sheep to provide wool, there would be less land for growing other food and a glut of lamb.

When crude oil is processed some sulphur is obtained. The sulphur can be made into sulphuric acid, for making detergents, synthetic fibres, fertilisers and for putting in car batteries.

You can get common salt directly from sea water or from dried up sea beds under the ground. This salt can be made into hydrochloric acid by industry as well as in your body. In industry salt is also made on a large scale into sodium hydroxide, chlorine and domestic bleach.

From the rocks of the earth's crust the chemical industry makes iron and steel, copper, aluminium, glass, cement and concrete. From these materials you can make cars, ships, planes and trains or you can build houses, factories, bridges and roads. You have to choose the right material for the purpose. You can describe some substances as synthetic and others as natural but like most classifications, the dividing line is sometimes hard to judge.

Chemistry by you

In chemistry you study the properties of substances. Most substances you find in nature are mixtures. So you may have to purify natural materials by separating these mixtures into their parts. For other experiments you may want to make known mixtures. At what temperature does a solid melt or a liquid boil? What happens when bread becomes toast, when oil reacts with sulphuric acid and then with sodium hydroxide, or when methane burns? What are the energy changes in these reactions? How fast do these reactions go? What are the structures of the substances involved? Can the properties of substances be explained by their structures? Can you make use of the information to control known things or to invent new substances?

Consider the substances mentioned in this introductory chapter. You may realise that sorting substances and types of changes into classes is an important way of making sense of all the information available. You can sort the substances into:

solids – nylon, steel, rubber, margarine, sodium chloride . . .
liquids – water, petrol, milk, fruit squash . . .
gases – air, chlorine, oxygen, methane . . .

These substances can also be sorted into:

elements – simple substances which cannot be broken down any
further by chemical reactions
compounds – substances formed by joining elements together in
chemical reactions
mixtures – elements and/or compounds put together but easily
separated again

and examples of these are:

elements – chlorine, oxygen, iron, aluminium, nitrogen . . .
compounds – nylon, Terylene, water, hydrochloric acid, sodium
hydroxide, ammonium nitrate, methane . . .
mixtures – air, steel, margarine, bread, milk, petrol, sea water . . .

An important classification of elements is into:

metals – iron, aluminium, copper . . .
non-metals – chlorine, oxygen, nitrogen . . .

There are several classifications of compounds such as:

acids – hydrochloric acid, sulphuric acid . . .
bases (including alkalis) – sodium hydroxide . . .
salts – sodium chloride, ammonium nitrate . . .

Other important classifications which apply to elements as well as to compounds are into:

oxidising substances – oxygen, chlorine, hydrochloric acid . . .
reducing substances – aluminium, methane . . .

and into

those which conduct electricity – aluminium, copper, hydrochloric acid . . .

those which do not conduct electricity – sulphur, water,
nylon . . .

Behind all these classifications are the theories of how the atoms
of elements are constructed and how they join together to make
compounds.

Solid, liquid or gas?
Element, compound or mixture?
Metal or non-metal?
Acid, base (alkali) or salt?
Oxidising or reducing substance?
Inorganic or organic substance?
Conducting or non-conducting substance?
Metallic, covalent or ionic bonding?

Fig. 3.   Eight questions that lead to general answers

1

Air

1.1 What's in the air?

The air, our atmosphere, is a mixture of many gases, water vapour and some dust. The two main gases are nitrogen (about four-fifths) and oxygen (about one-fifth), which together make up over 99% of dried air. All the other gases add up to give us the last 1%: these minor ones include argon, carbon dioxide and neon.

To check the proportion of oxygen by experiment, a sample of air can be pushed to and fro over hot copper, using the apparatus shown in Figure 1.1. The copper removes the oxygen from the air by reacting with it. The gas syringes measure the volume of air in the apparatus before and after heating the copper, so the volume of oxygen removed can be worked out. Another method is to burn phosphorus or let iron rust in a trapped sample of air. The common experiment of burning a candle in a closed jar does not give an accurate result.

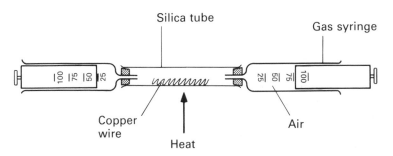

Fig. 1.1. Checking the proportion of oxygen in air

The presence of carbon dioxide in air is shown by blowing air through calcium hydroxide solution (limewater) – it becomes cloudy, see Figure 21.2. The presence of water vapour (about 1% usually) can be shown by the tests described in Section 2.4.

1.2 Separating the gases in air

To separate the carbon dioxide from air, the air can be sucked through sodium hydroxide solution which will form sodium hydrogencarbonate solution. If this solution is added to hydrochloric acid then the carbon dioxide escapes again.

To separate water vapour from air, air can be sucked through a tube cooled by ice and salt. Water will condense in the tube. Alternatively, the air can be sucked through anhydrous calcium chloride (white lumps) which will become hydrated (clear colourless crystals, then a solution). When hydrated calcium chloride is heated it loses the water it had gained.

In industry, water vapour and carbon dioxide are removed from air by compression and cooling. The remaining air is cooled until it forms a liquid. (The principles of doing this are the same as in your fridge: a compressed gas expands through a valve and so cools.) The liquid air is distilled and separates into its parts according to their boiling points: first the nitrogen boils off at $-196 \,°C$ (77 K if we measure from the absolute zero of temperature), then the oxygen boils at $-183 \,°C$ (90 K).

In the laboratory, oxygen can be separated from nitrogen by passing the air over hot copper or iron. The metal forms a solid oxide. The nitrogen left still contains the noble gases (mainly argon and neon) but these do not affect the tests you can do, see Section 17.7.

1.3 How pure is the air we breathe?

Air is a mixture: its composition varies slightly from day to day and place to place. As you go up in the air it becomes less dense and on high mountains you need to carry a supply of oxygen. Planes must provide air at normal pressure for the crew and passengers to breathe.

When we breathe in, the proportion of oxygen in the air is about

20% and that of carbon dioxide about 0·03%. When we breathe out the proportion of oxygen has gone down to 16% and that of carbon dioxide has gone up to 4%. Exhaled air has enough oxygen to give artificial respiration to another person, but we would not want to breathe it in all the time. However, we are saved from being suffocated by too much carbon dioxide by photosynthesis, see Section 7.1.

Since the beginning of the Industrial Revolution nearly 300 years ago, the proportion of carbon dioxide in the air has increased. This extra carbon dioxide is produced by the burning of fuels. Some of it also dissolves in rainwater and in the sea. A possible side effect of more carbon dioxide is the 'greenhouse' effect. Is the earth getting slightly warmer because carbon dioxide traps infra-red radiation from the sun? If so, will the polar ice caps melt a little quicker and the level of the sea rise?

When fuels do not burn completely, some carbon (soot) and poisonous carbon monoxide are produced. The soot settles as dust. In sunlight the carbon monoxide is soon oxidised to carbon dioxide. If fuels do not burn at all, unburnt hydrocarbons escape into the air. Rotting vegetation also gives off some natural gas into the air. These hydrocarbons are oxidised in sunlight in the upper atmosphere where some of the oxygen (O_2) has changed into ozone (O_3). (To oxidise means to add on or react with oxygen, see Chapter 24.)

When a blast furnace makes iron, and again when iron is made into steel, a lot of dust is produced which is expensive to trap. Quarrying rocks also makes a lot of dust but this dust is impossible to trap. Sometimes there are unexpected advantages in pollution control. A lead factory in London found that the dust it trapped contained so much lead that the control equipment soon paid for itself and made a profit.

Coal and oil both contain some sulphur and their combustion gives sulphur dioxide. At first the blame for damage to trees fell on this gas which could directly affect growing plants (dry deposition). When sulphur dioxide dissolves in water it forms sulphurous acid (H_2SO_3) which is easily oxidised to sulphuric acid (H_2SO_4). This gives wet deposition or **acid rain**. Rainwater is naturally acidic because of dissolved carbon dioxide but the presence of sulphuric acid means that the rain is even more acidic. Thus it may affect the stonework of buildings and corrode metals.

Two other pollutants of the atmosphere arise chiefly from transport. The first is nitrogen monoxide (NO), formed inside engines when they get very hot. This gas quickly forms nitrogen dioxide (NO_2); together they are often quoted as NO_x. Nitrogen dioxide also causes acid rain and its reactions with hydrocarbons and ozone in sunlight may cause some of the damage to trees. An advantage of nitrogen dioxide is that it dissolves in water to give nitric acid which is a fertiliser.

The second pollutant from transport comes from tetraethyl-lead which is added to most petrol to increase the power of car engines. The proportion added is less than it was a few years ago and some alternatives have been found. The presence of this lead compound helps the petrol burn smoothly in the engine but the consequence is that lead and some of its compounds are sprayed out from the exhaust. Lead is a nerve poison: the dangers are greatest to people in towns and especially to young children.

In some cities, for example Los Angeles, Athens and Tokyo, cold air is sometimes trapped in low lying areas surrounded by hills, with warm air above. When there is no wind the pollutants in the air react in sunlight to give 'photochemical smog'. A smog is smoke plus fog. In the USA car exhausts are fitted with catalytic converters to try to reduce the amount of pollution. These converters also reduce the power of the car engine and make the car more expensive. In Greece when pollution is troublesome, people with odd numbered cars are allowed to drive only on odd numbered dates. In Japan the police on traffic duty have been known to do 20 minutes on duty and then refresh themselves from a cylinder of oxygen.

Bronchitis has been called the English disease. Is it caused by our damp atmosphere reacting with the acidic gases, sulphur dioxide and nitrogen dioxide, to cause respiratory irritation? London used to be famous for its 'pea soup' fogs. In 1952 there was one that lasted several days and it was calculated that 4000 more people died than would have been expected to during the next few weeks. This led to the Clean Air Act of 1956 which set up smokeless zones, see Figure 1.2. Gradually the air of our towns became cleaner and so did our buildings, we got more sunlight, especially in winter, plants grew better and people suffered less from respiratory diseases. There have been lots of benefits from the Act.

(*a*) Public Records Office before cleaning.

(*b*) Public Records Office after cleaning.

Fig. 1.2. London before and after the Clean Air Act

2

Water

2.1 It's raining

It's raining up in the hills as I write this chapter. The clouds are rolling in from the west and getting cooler as they climb so the water vapour in them falls as rain. My tap water comes from a spring on the side of the hill and I filter it before drinking. Most of the water flows down into the river. Downstream the water authority takes some of the river water. They treat it more thoroughly before supplying it to homes and factories. By the time the river reaches the sea it has dissolved many things and had many others thrown into it. From the sea the water can evaporate again, leaving behind most of the impurities. More clouds form and the **water cycle** continues (see Figure 7.2).

Water covers 70% of the earth's surface. It is trapped as ice and snow in cold regions. Sea water contains about 27 g of sodium chloride and about 8 g of other salts in every litre. River water is often hard because of dissolved minerals, see Section 3.1. Most water contains gases dissolved from the air. Fish depend on the dissolved oxygen. The rotting of many substances also depends on this oxygen. Scientists measure the 'Biological Oxygen Demand' of natural water, which is how much oxygen it absorbs during storage for 5 days in the dark at 20 °C. This is measured in milligrams of oxygen per litre of water. The result should be below 20 mg/l for water of reasonable quality.

The average person uses over 150 litres of water every day: one-third for washing, one-third down the toilet, and the rest for drinking and in many small ways. A lot of the water we use does not need to be drinkable but the expense of installing a second water system is too great to justify doing it.

Fig. 2.1. Clouds

2.2 Water pollution

There are many substances which dissolve naturally in river water. The problem with water is that it is the best solvent known and many other substances will dissolve (or mix) in it.

The farmer puts fertilisers on his fields to grow more grass and wheat. If it rains very heavily soon after, then some of the fertiliser gets into the river. This speeds the growth of plants in the river, they eventually rot and the river becomes starved of oxygen. This series of processes is called **eutrophication**. From time to time the farmer has to dip his sheep and cattle or spray his fields with herbicides and pesticides to keep down the weeds and insects. The chemicals needed are very dangerous to us and so much care is needed to prevent them getting into rivers. To feed his cattle in winter the farmer may store silage (freshly mown grass) and in winter he may keep his cattle as well as his chickens indoors. The effluent (waste liquid) from all these places must not be allowed to get directly into the river. We must have food, but growing plants and rearing animals causes many problems.

Many of the things we use and foods we eat are made or processed in factories. Most factories have some waste disposal problem. There are special sites where dangerous rubbish can be thrown away safely under supervision. When aluminium is made, the purification of the ore (bauxite) gives a lot of iron(III) oxide which is mixed with sodium hydroxide – the disposal of this is called the 'red mud problem'.

In old houses the water pipes are often made of lead. This does not matter very much when the water is hard but is serious when the water is soft, as some of the lead will dissolve in soft water. Lead is a cumulative poison and so in places such as Glasgow which have soft water it is important to replace lead by plastic or copper for water pipes.

Fig. 2.2.   Beckton sewage works (East London)

Too often the problems of pollution are thought to be due to industry or farming. The biggest problem though is people. Ever since people gathered in towns and cities the disposal of sewage has been important. Sewage may be 99% water but the other 1% needs a lot of treatment. The sewage is filtered to remove large pieces of rubbish (rags, toys, etc.) and then passes into settling tanks where a lot of 'sludge' is precipitated. There are bacteria in sewage which will gradually break it down. Blowing in air and warming speeds up the reactions. As the sewage ferments, natural gas escapes and this can be burnt as a fuel to reduce the running costs of the treatment plant. Then the sewage passes into more settling tanks where it deposits 'humus', and the effluent is then clean enough to be put back into the river. Some sewage works sell the sludge for use as a grassland fertiliser because it is rich in nitrogen and phosphorus compounds, others just dump it. The use of detergents instead of soap has increased the proportions of nitrogen and phosphorus compounds in waste water.

2.3 Drinking water

Having read the previous section, do you still want a drink of water? It is vital for your life. You must drink over a litre every day even if you flavour it and drink milk, tea, coffee, squash or Coke. Your body will extract another litre of water from the food you eat. In the less developed countries people walk long distances to find drinking water. They do not always succeed in finding pure water and most of the disease in the world comes from water-borne infection. In the UK we are lucky because we can get water from a tap and it is drinkable, whether we use it for ourselves, to clean the car or in the garden.

Water is taken from the river as far upstream as possible. It is led into a reservoir where it stands still for days. During this time soil and other solids settle to the bottom. A trace of copper(II) sulphate may be put into the water to kill off algae. The water from the reservoir is filtered through gravel and coarse sand. Then it is filtered slowly through fine sand. The final stage is to kill off germs by treating the water with chlorine or ozone. Both of these reagents oxidise the germs. The water then goes into covered storage reservoirs and does not come out into the open until you turn on the tap.

In some drinking water there are fluorine compounds present naturally. It has been found that this reduces dental decay, particularly in young children. Therefore some water authorities add a small proportion of sodium fluoride to the water they supply; however, some people object to this addition.

2.4 Tests for water

You cannot see steam coming out of a kettle. What you see are droplets of water forming as it cools. A fog, a mist and a cloud also consist of droplets of water. When water cools still further you get ice, frost and snow. Water is the only substance that has different names for the gas, the liquid and the solid forms.

If you see a colourless liquid you may think that it is water or that it contains water. There are two ways you can test for the presence of water.

(a) Anhydrous copper(II) sulphate is white. When water is added to it, it turns to blue hydrated crystals and heat is given out. (Anhydrous means without water; hydrated means containing water.)

(b) Anhydrous cobalt(II) chloride is blue. When water is added to it, it turns to deep pink (purple) hydrated crystals. Again heat is given out.

These two tests do not distinguish between pure water and water in mixtures. To check whether water is pure there are three tests that you can do and one that you must not do.

(a) Measure the boiling point. This is 100 °C at the standard pressure of 101 kilopascals (or 1000 millibars as the weathermen say). The temperature in the water must be measured. The temperature of steam above an aqueous solution will always be 100 °C. (Aqueous means dissolved in water.) The temperature in the water will be above 100 °C if there are some solids dissolved in the water.

(b) Measure the freezing point. This is 0 °C. The temperature will be less than 0 °C if there are some solids dissolved in the water. Freezing points are hardly affected by pressure.

(c) Measure the density, using a hydrometer. The density of pure water is 1 gram per millilitre. This test may not be easy to do accurately.

(*d*) Tasting is **not** safe – don't take risks.

2.5 Chemical properties of water

Water dissolves many substances, for example salt, in a simple way. Many other substances have a chemical reaction with water. The reactions of metals with water can be used to put them in an order called the activity series, see Chapter 25.

The electrolysis of water is discussed in Section 14.2. Although ionic substances such as sulphuric acid have to be put in the water to make it conduct electricity, it is the water which decomposes to give 2 volumes of hydrogen and 1 volume of oxygen. The formula of a molecule of water is H_2O.

The formula of water and the mass of its molecules do not explain many of its peculiar properties. If you compare water with many other hydrogen compounds you are left with a puzzle. Some of the properties of water that are much higher than expected are: melting point, boiling point, the energy needed to change solid into liquid and liquid into gas, the energy needed to warm it by 1 °C, the ability to act as a solvent. To explain many of these properties we talk of a special type of bonding – **hydrogen bonding**. This also occurs in

Fig. 2.3. Cooling towers at West Burton power station

ammonia and hydrogen fluoride but not in methane (natural gas), phosphine (PH_3), hydrogen sulphide or hydrogen chloride. Hydrogen bonding holds molecules together. It is much weaker than covalent or ionic bonding (see Chapters 30 and 31). It causes ice to have a lower density than water so icebergs float and ice forms at the *top* of a pond. These odd properties of water mean that aquatic life in ponds and rivers survives during a hard winter, safe beneath the ice. Without hydrogen bonding the oceans would evaporate, DNA (the molecule that carries life from one generation to the next) would fall apart, and even we would evaporate!

2.6 Uses of water

Water is used on a large scale in many industries. Using water and natural gas, hydrogen is manufactured and used to make ammonia and fertilisers, see Sections 17.9 and 18.3. Water is needed to convert ethene into ethanol (alcohol), see Section 19.3. Water is used as a coolant, a solvent or to move materials around in many industries: coke, rayon, wool, cotton, steel, paper, sugar, many electrolytic processes and electricity generation. Steam is used to heat materials in some processes and ice is used to cool others.

Pure water has to be made by distillation or ion exchange, see Sections 12.3 and 3.2. In the Middle East and some other places distillation is the only way to make enough drinking water. In laboratories pure water is needed to make many solutions. Pure water is needed to cool the direct-current electricity cable between England and France. It is used to wash transistors. The motorist needs it to top up his battery.

As well as advantages, there are disadvantages in water being the best solvent we know; it is rare for water to be pure enough for all those who want to drink or use it.

3

Hard Water

3.1 Try soap

A hard water is one that does not lather easily with soap.

You may have noticed at home or on holiday that when you wash your hands there is a lot of scum in the basin of water. You need more soap in some districts than in others to get a lather. Look inside a kettle. Is there a white solid (fur) round the edge or on the heating element? This is another sign that the water is hard. If you find some white solid, tap off a bit and test it with vinegar. It should fizz. The bubbles are carbon dioxide, which can be tested for as shown in Figure 21.2.

There are two ways in which water becomes hard. The first way is that rainwater runs over rocks made of calcium sulphate, which occurs in nature as minerals called gypsum and anhydrite. Very slowly the minerals dissolve. A very dilute solution of calcium sulphate is produced and this does not change if it is boiled: the water is permanently hard.

The second way depends on rainwater being very slightly acidic because it has carbon dioxide dissolved in it. Very slowly this rainwater will dissolve rocks such as chalk, limestone and marble. Many of our hills are made of these rocks which are all forms of calcium carbonate, see Figure 3.1. A chemical reaction occurs:

calcium carbonate + water + carbon dioxide

$\rightarrow$ calcium hydrogencarbonate solution

This solution is very dilute. If it is boiled the reaction is reversed and the calcium carbonate reforms as a solid – this is the 'fur' you find in kettles. The water is temporarily hard. After boiling, the water will lather readily with soap. The hardness has been destroyed.

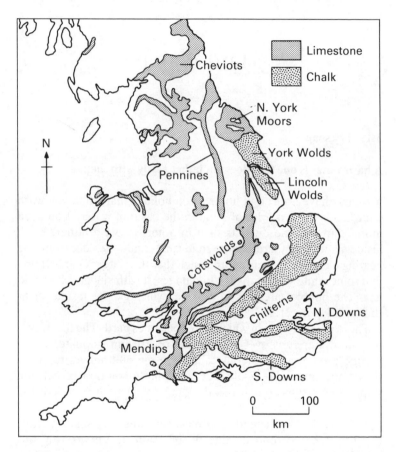

Fig. 3.1.   Limestone and chalk hills in England and Wales

Many natural waters contain both types of hardness. In some areas magnesium compounds cause the water to be hard. Most tap water in the UK is hard. It is good for us because we need calcium for our bones and teeth and for blood clotting. There is less heart disease in hard water districts than in soft water districts. Hard water has a taste but you will find it difficult to describe it, however flat or insipid you think distilled water is. Hard water is needed for brewing beer and lager. If you have lead pipes in your house then hard water forms insoluble lead compounds on the inner surface so you are less likely to be poisoned. There is even an environmental bonus from living in a limestone or chalk district. You will find caves with stalagmites (growing up) and stalactites (growing down) formed by the reverse of the reaction on page 13.

Fig. 3.2. Stalagmites and stalactites in a Cheddar cave

Hard water has obvious disadvantages. It wastes soap and the scum must be rinsed away thoroughly when washing your hands and clothes. Hard water spoils the feel of fabrics and causes problems in dyeing fabrics and in tanning leather. If the hardness is temporary the other major disadvantage is the formation of calcium carbonate whenever the water is heated. If your kettle is furred up, fuel is wasted trying to warm the water through the fur. In an industrial boiler the energy losses will be greater and in a pipe (where it is called scale) the consequence could be a total blockage. At big power stations all the water is softened before it goes into the boilers. Some disadvantages can be avoided by using a soapless detergent, but most still remain.

3.2   How to soften water

To soften water you must either

(*a*) swap the calcium compounds for sodium compounds, or
(*b*) completely remove the calcium compounds from the water.

In a dishwasher or water softener at home the first method is used. You start with a substance called an 'ion-exchange resin' (an ion is an electrically charged particle). This resin is a sodium compound and only the sodium part of it reacts with and dissolves in the hard water. The hard water flows past the resin and becomes a very dilute solution of sodium compounds instead of calcium compounds. The water is now soft. Then you regenerate the resin by letting salt (sodium chloride) solution flow past the used resin. The rinsing solution, which becomes calcium chloride solution, is drained away.

Another method used at home is to shake a few crystals of 'bath salts' into your bath water or of 'washing soda' into your washing water. Both these substances are forms of sodium carbonate and cause a precipitate of small crystals of calcium carbonate that can be rinsed away. (A precipitate is an insoluble solid formed from soluble substances.) The solution that you wash in is a very dilute solution of sodium hydrogencarbonate and/or sodium sulphate. A third method sometimes used at home is to use 'Calgon'. As its name implies, the calcium has gone – gone into hiding in a complex phosphate but without giving any precipitate.

Distillation is the method used to remove all the calcium compounds from water, and this can be used for both types of hardness. Boiling the water and filtering will only remove the calcium that is present as temporary hardness. A method used by some water authorities is Clark's method (Thomas Clark, 1801–67, Scotland). Calcium hydroxide is added to the water to cause the precipitation

of calcium carbonate. His method only works for temporary hardness but is useful if this is excessive.

Mixtures of ion-exchange resins can be used to 'demineralise'
water completely so that it is as pure or purer than distilled water.

4

Minerals and Factories

4.1 Minerals

Oxygen is the most abundant element in the rocks of the earth's crust, 45·0%. It is followed by silicon 27·0%, aluminium 8·0%, iron 5·8%, calcium 5·1%, magnesium 2·8%, sodium 2·3% and potassium 1·7%. All these elements are 'locked up' in compounds and some of the compounds are very hard to decompose. The weather helps us to some extent because rainwater and carbon dioxide react slowly with many rocks, converting them into other rocks from which it is easier to extract substances.

It may make up nearly half of the rocks of the earth's crust, but the best way of manufacturing oxygen is not from the rocks but from the air. Silicon is made starting from sand (silicon dioxide) and aluminium from bauxite (impure hydrated aluminium oxide). In all these examples the more common rocks are too difficult to decompose cheaply. To get silicon and aluminium we process the weathered rocks, which are simpler compounds.

A **mineral** is a naturally occurring substance which has definite physical properties and chemical composition. An **ore** is a mineral or a group of minerals from which a metal or another useful substance can economically be extracted. Quartz and asbestos are minerals. Sand and bauxite are ores.

Figure 3.1 shows where there are limestone and chalk hills in England and Wales. On those hills there are many quarries. Nearby there are often factories for making cement. The largest quarry is near Buxton, see Figure 4.1, and trainloads of calcium carbonate are taken to factories in Cheshire, which convert it into sodium carbonate.

Fig. 4.1. Quarry for limestone at Buxton

Four-fifths of the common salt (sodium chloride) we use in the UK comes from Cheshire. There is one mine where it is obtained as a solid, just as coal is mined. Most of the salt is obtained by solution mining: water is pumped down, it dissolves the salt and then the solution (brine) is pumped back to the surface. Often the brine is used directly in factories which make it into sodium hydroxide and chlorine, see Section 14.4.

Some iron compounds are mined in the East Midlands, but we import most of our iron ore from Canada, Brazil and Australia, to be processed in south Wales, by the Clyde estuary, in north east England and by the Humber estuary.

4.2 Where do you build a factory?

Are all the materials needed found in one place? In 1709 Abraham Darby used Shropshire coal to make coke and then heated the coke with local iron ore to make iron. The Industrial Revolution had started. Today Shropshire is not important for iron or coal – the iron-making industry is usually near the ports where iron ore is imported. The coal industry has found more economic seams elsewhere in the UK. Steel is often made where a lot of scrap is available, for example near London and Birmingham, as well as near the blast furnaces where iron is made.

Sometimes factories are built where the supply of fuel is good. Small factories for making aluminium have existed in Scotland for many years near hydroelectric power plants. More recently, large factories have been built for making aluminium next to a coal mine in north east England and near a nuclear power station in Anglesey. For many industries the supply of fresh water or cooling water is just as important as the supply of fuel.

Do you put a factory next to a town so you have a large labour force available, or does a town grow up near to a factory because people do not like to travel far to go to work? Some of the early mill

Fig. 4.2. Aerial view of the petroleum refinery (Shell) at Teesport

owners built model villages for their workers, for example the Gregs at Styal, near Manchester, and the Cadburys at Bourneville, near Birmingham. Farmers often provide cottages for their workers. Many coal mine owners built houses for their workers in the 1800s. Towns like Runcorn and Warrington have grown up by the side of the factories which make Cheshire salt into other chemicals, using Derbyshire limestone and south Lancashire coal.

When you have made things in factories, the waste products have to be disposed of safely. In the past too many quarries and mines have had large, ugly waste heaps beside them. Tipping coal waste into the sea in north east England does not improve the colour of the sea, but some people make a living from collecting pieces of coal from the beaches nearby and selling them. The spoil from some mines in the Pennines is now being processed again to look for other minerals. Today, after opencast mining for coal or iron ore or even after laying a pipeline for gas, a lot of effort goes into restoring the landscape.

After a factory has made its goods they have to be sold. Do you build your factory near to the market, the people who are going to use your products? Or do you build your factory elsewhere and then spend a lot of money distributing the goods across the country or to other parts of the world? For materials like sulphuric acid there are many factories close to the users. For materials like medicines, there are only a few factories and then the materials are distributed widely. Would you like a nuclear power station built next door? Or do you prefer to see pylon lines strung across the countryside to bring you electricity? Look around your district to see what industry is there. Which reasons for its location do you think were the most important?

5

Fuels

5.1 Today and tomorrow?

Two hundred years ago most people used wood fires to keep their homes warm. Then came the Industrial Revolution and coal became freely available. Less than 150 years ago Edwin Drake (1819–80, USA) drilled the first oil well. From 1900 to 1970 the use of oil doubled every 10 years. The first nuclear power stations for peaceful purposes, built to use uranium as fuel, were opened in the UK and USSR about 30 years ago. Natural gas has only been used widely in the last 20 years: previously gas was made from coal. When natural gas runs out coal may be used again for making a fuel gas. Coal, oil and gas are *primary* sources of energy because they are

Year	Coal %	Oil %	Gas %	Hydro-electric %	Nuclear %	Total in exajoules $(10^{18} J)$
1865						0.50
1880						0.94
1900	94	4	1	1	0	2.28
1920	87	9	2	2	0	4.22
1940	75	18	4	3	0	5.16
1960	52	31	15	2	0	11.82
1980	29	43	20	6	2	28.90
1985	31	38	20	7	5	31.02

Fig. 5.1. World energy – percentages supplied by main fuels

used directly to provide energy. Most electricity is a *secondary* source of energy: it is the result of the combustion of coal. Hydro-electric power is a minor source of primary energy and will soon be overtaken by nuclear power.

The rosy picture of the increasing use of energy was shattered in the 1970s by the rise in the price of oil. Then people realised that the reserves of the fossil fuels (coal, oil and gas) were finite (limited). What are the consequences? The first answer is to 'save it': use fuels more efficiently, turn off fires and machines when not in use, insulate buildings so that warmth is conserved, and so on. The second answer is to find other sources of energy. Can sunlight, wind, water or radioactivity provide an economic alternative?

The fossil fuels were made from natural materials millions of years ago. We use them faster than we discover new reserves. Their use may follow the sort of pattern shown in Figure 5.2. We have used a small proportion of the known reserves of coal, a larger proportion of our gas and a still larger proportion of our oil. So oil may be in short supply in 40 years, natural gas in 80 years and coal in 160 years from now, depending on whether we discover more reserves and how much we use each year.

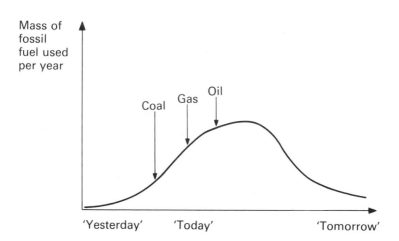

Fig. 5.2. A wide view of energy

5.2   Coal

About 300 million years ago, in the Carboniferous Period, the continents were nearer the equator. Many large tree-like ferns grew, died and fell to the ground. As living plants they were about 44% carbon. When they died, they rotted and got buried. The chemical changes often happened in the absence of air. The proportion of carbon increased as water escaped. The changes slowly gave us:

	Percentage carbon
peat (when dried)	60
lignite, a soft brown coal	67
sub-bituminous coal (cannel coal)	86
bituminous coal (household coal)	88
anthracite (hard coal)	94

The continents have moved and most of the coal mined today is in China, USA, USSR, Poland and India. Most of the known reserves are in the USA and USSR. Figure 5.3 shows where coal is found in the British Isles.

In chemical composition, bituminous coal contains approximately one carbon atom for every hydrogen atom (the other main element is oxygen).The coal may need washing to remove some other rocks but it is then ready to be burnt. The mining of coal may cause the land above to subside. The cleaning of the coal has often left large spoil heaps near the mines. In the UK a tenth of the coal comes from opencast mining. If the landscape is restored afterwards it looks better and is less dangerous. Yesterday's spoil heaps are slowly disappearing.

When coal is burnt most of it forms carbon dioxide and steam. Some of it does not burn completely so it forms carbon monoxide or escapes as carbon (soot). There is a tiny proportion of sulphur in coal. The sulphur becomes sulphur dioxide. The combustion of coal in power stations is more efficient than in many small fires at home and there is less pollution. Today four-fifths of the coal in the UK is used to produce electricity. The soot can easily be trapped but it is more difficult to deal with the gaseous pollutants that escape into the atmosphere, such as carbon monoxide and sulphur dioxide.

If cooling water is discharged into a river it causes thermal pollution. The hotter river water dissolves less oxygen, so many fish find it harder to survive and sewage decomposes more slowly. Also, weeds may grow faster and will hinder the flow of water.

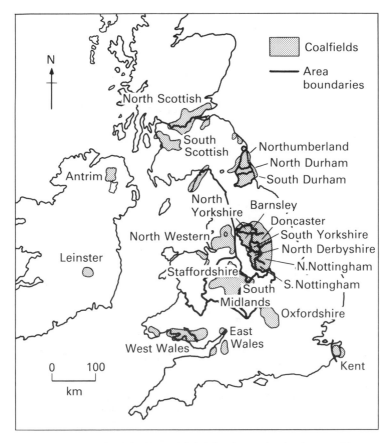

Fig. 5.3. Coal in the British Isles (none in the far north)

Today the main reason for heating coal in retorts (big steel boxes lined with firebrick) is to make coke. Before the arrival of natural gas the main reason was to make coal gas. Without air the coal does not burn – instead it decomposes at 600–1200 °C. The residue is coke (almost pure carbon) or another smokeless fuel, depending on the temperature. The residue is used as a fuel but the problem of sulphur dioxide forming still remains. A lot of coke is used to reduce iron oxide to iron in blast furnaces, see Section 15.2. The gases that escape from the coal are purified by removing tar (used to make many substances as well as for road tar), ammonia (for fertilisers), benzene (for making many chemicals), naphthalene (for making dyes and other chemicals) and hydrogen sulphide (for making sulphur and sulphuric acid).

The coal gas left is now burnt directly, but it used to be processed further so that it was about 50% hydrogen and 30% methane before it was sold. If coal is to be a main fuel when oil and gas run short, then new ways of using it may be needed. Research is going on to produce better varieties of coal gas and also to turn coal into a liquid fuel, like petrol.

5.3 Oil

Oil was formed underground millions of years ago from rotting plant and animal remains, usually in the sea. The oil may seep through rocks which are porous but then it is usually trapped by other rocks. Often it is found with natural gas. Oil is a mixture of many compounds of hydrogen and carbon (the **hydrocarbons**), some of which are straight chains, some branched chains and others ring compounds, see Chapter 19. A few of the compounds contain sulphur. Unlike coal, oxygen is absent from these compounds. On average there are two atoms of hydrogen for every atom of carbon in oil.

The main producers of crude oil (petroleum) are the USSR, USA, Saudi Arabia, Mexico, UK, China and Iran. The main reserves are in Saudi Arabia, the rest of the Middle East, Mexico and the USA. The situation in the UK is interesting and disturbing, because almost no oil was produced until 1975, by 1980 we were self-sufficient, and since 1983 we have been able to export one-third of our production. But our proved reserves are very small. Will it all be gone by the year 2030, or will we find some other sources? See Figure 5.4.

Crude oil when it comes out of the ground is a useless mixture of useful substances. In a refinery it is given a primary distillation – it is heated to about 400 °C and most of it becomes a gas. The gas passes

Fig. 5.4. Oil in and around the British Isles

into a fractionating column. This is a tall tower in which there are many trays of bubble caps. In a bubble cap gases going up are forced to bubble through liquids that are flowing down, see Figure 5.5. The top of the tower is cool and the bottom is hot. The liquids can be drained off from some of the trays. The crude oil is separated into **fractions** – smaller mixtures of substances which have similar boiling points, see Figure 5.6. Fractions with higher boiling points have higher viscosity (resistance to flow) and are more difficult to burn.

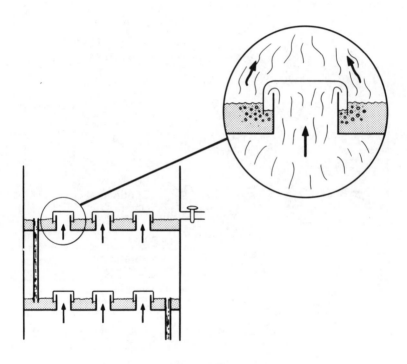

Fig. 5.5. Inside a fractionating column, showing a single bubble cap

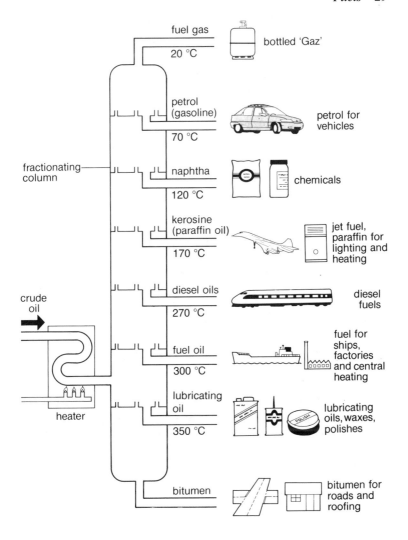

Fig. 5.6. The fractions of crude oil

Name of fraction	Approximate number of carbon atoms	Approximate boiling point/°C	Uses
Gases	1–4	less than 40	fuels, solvents
Petrol (gasoline) and naphtha	5–10	40–190	fuel, making other chemicals
Kerosine (paraffin)	11–14	190–260	fuels for homes and planes
Diesel oil	15–19	260–330	light fuel oil
Lubricating oil	19–30	330–400	lubricants, medicinal paraffin, paraffin wax
Bitumen	over 30	over 400	heavy fuel oil, asphalt

The primary distillation does not give us the different fractions in the proportions we want at any time (our needs vary from winter to summer). The second stage in the processing of oil is the **catalytic cracking** of large molecules into small molecules. The catalyst often used is aluminium oxide at about 500 °C. A result of cracking is the formation of unsaturated compounds, see Section 19.3.

A possible third stage is 'reforming' molecules: straight-chain molecules can be changed into branched-chain molecules. This is important in producing petrol. An alternative third stage is polymerisation, see Section 20.1.

Compared to coal, oil has the disadvantage that it needs a lot of processing. Oil has the advantages that it gives a more useful variety of fuels and it can be made into a large variety of other substances. Many people say that we are wasting it by using it as a fuel when the supply is so limited.

5.4 Natural gas

Natural gas (methane) is formed when plants rot in the absence of air (anaerobic decomposition). If you disturb the bottom of a pond, bubbles of gas rise to the surface and escape. Some gas is obtained from old quarries which have been filled with rubbish and then covered over with soil. Some is obtained from coal mines and other inland boreholes. Most of the UK's natural gas comes from under the North Sea and the Irish Sea, see Figure 5.7.

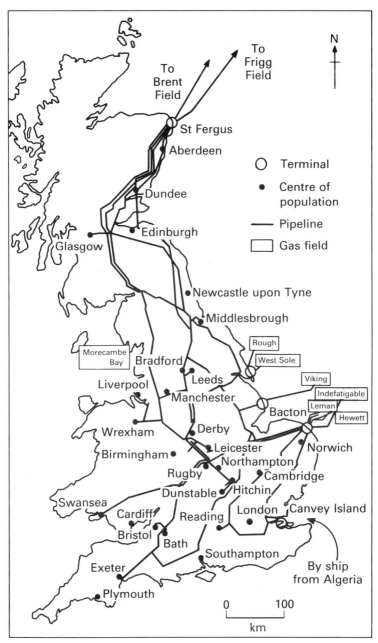

Fig. 5.7. Natural gas in and around the UK

Since 1967 when natural gas was first piped in from North Sea wells, the manufacture of coal gas has stopped (except when making coke). The main producers of natural gas are the USSR, USA, Canada and the Netherlands. Natural gas sometimes contains very small proportions of other substances such as ethane (C_2H_6). It requires almost no processing except checking that it is dry. For safety reasons it is given a smell, by adding traces of some sulphur compounds.

The UK imports some of its natural gas from Algeria. When the gas is turned into a liquid its volume shrinks tremendously and it is then shipped in refrigerated tanks. At Canvey Island in the River Thames estuary it is fed into the national gas grid. There are two ways of storing natural gas: as a liquid and as a compressed gas, both of which have their advantages.

The combustion of natural gas gives carbon dioxide and steam. There is no serious problem of sulphur dioxide pollution. As in the combustion of all fuels, there is the danger that carbon monoxide will form if there is not enough air for complete combustion.

5.5 Are there alternatives?

Yes there are, but at the moment most of them are not economic or easy to produce on a large scale.

If you sink a mine into the **earth** you find that the temperature of the rocks increases as you go down. There are parts of the world where this is more noticeable than others. Tests are being done in Cornwall and Hampshire. Cold water is pumped down one hole, the rocks heat it, then it is pumped up a second hole. In northern Italy this 'geothermal' energy is converted to electricity which is used to run the railways. In Iceland and New Zealand there are many natural geysers supplying hot water.

Windmills were originally used for pumping water or for grinding corn. They are now being used in the Orkneys, in Kent and at Cardigan Bay to generate electricity, see Figure 5.8.

The energy of the **sun** can be trapped in several ways.

(*a*) By growing plants and fermenting them to give alcohol which can be used as a fuel. In this way Brazil economises on petrol.

(*b*) By letting the sun warm water in solar panels on the roof of a

Fig. 5.8. A windmill being used to generate electricity

building. Many people now use this method of boosting the temperature of their hot water supply. An alternative is to use mirrors to focus the sun's rays onto a boiler which then produces steam to generate electricity. This is being tried in the Pyrenées (France) and in Arizona (USA).

(c) By letting the sun's rays fall on silicon wafers, which give a direct supply of electricity. This method is very expensive now but is used in some calculators.

(d) If a way can be found to make hydrogen from water economically, then hydrogen could be the fuel of the future. At the moment it is only used as a fuel in space rockets. Hydrogen has disadvantages such as its low density and explosive nature.

Water has always provided a natural source of energy.

(a) Hydroelectric power is used on a large scale in some countries such as Norway, Canada, Scotland and the USA. Other countries lack the rainfall or the steep rivers.

(*b*) There is a tidal barrage at La Rance (near St Malo, France). The incoming tide turns turbines which generate electricity. The water is trapped by the barrage and released when the tide has gone out, thus turning the turbines again, see Figure 5.9. This scheme has been suggested for the Severn estuary in the UK and for other places.

(*c*) Pumped storage is not really an alternative, but it is the only way of having extra electricity available at peak times without big, idle power stations. It is used in North Wales and in Scotland. At peak times water flows downhill from one reservoir to another, generating electricity. At quiet times the water is pumped back uphill. Unfortunately more electricity is used in stage two than is generated in stage one.

(*d*) The up and down motion of the waves can be used to generate electricity. Various devices such as mechanical ducks, air bags and so on have been suggested.

Fig. 5.9.   The tidal barrage at La Rance (France)

6

Making Electricity

6.1 Primary cells

If you put two different metals or a metal and a stick of carbon (graphite) into some salt solution and then connect them by a copper wire, an electric current flows. You can use an ammeter to measure the current. It may be a very small current and it may quickly decrease to zero. Amaze your friends by trying it with a lemon instead of salt solution. A better instrument to use is a voltmeter: it has a high resistance and so there are fewer experimental problems. Suitable metals to try are copper, iron, magnesium and zinc.

When you put two metals into a conducting solution such as salty water, dilute sulphuric acid or sodium hydroxide solution, you have made a voltaic or galvanic **cell**. Chemical reactions are occurring and some of them are complex. These chemical reactions cause the electric current to flow in the copper wire from one metal to the other. It is a **direct current**, a one-way current. This voltaic cell is a primary cell because the reactions cannot be reversed and the cell is useless as soon as one metal has corroded away. Most dry batteries as used in torches, personal stereos, pocket radios and calculators are primary cells.

A cell is one unit, a battery is made of several cells. You will find that a cell usually has + and − marks. Sometimes the positive end has red plastic on the connecting screw and the negative end has black plastic on the connecting screw. The 'conventional current' flows from the positive to the negative sides of the cell through a copper wire. This convention was started before people knew what an electric current really was. Today we would describe it as a stream of electrons, which are tiny negatively charged particles, and they flow in the opposite direction to the conventional current.

6.2 Secondary cells and others

In a secondary cell it is possible to reverse the chemical reactions by connecting the terminals to a low-voltage power supply, so you can recharge the cell for further use. The best example of a secondary cell is a car battery. A car battery is made of six cells, each of which generates electricity at 2 volts. The negative plate in each cell is lead and the positive plate is lead(IV) oxide on a lead grid. The solution between the plates is moderately concentrated sulphuric acid which is very corrosive, so be careful. Water slowly evaporates from the battery, so the battery must be topped up with distilled (pure) water from time to time. You can check a car battery by measuring the density of the acid with a hydrometer: it should be about 1.28 g/ml, but decreases with use.

Sunlight (solar energy) can be converted directly into electrical energy by photoelectric or photovoltaic cells made of silicon. At the moment this is an expensive way of making electricity but the cost is justified when used for instruments for space rockets. Some alarm systems and crowd-counting instruments use a light beam or an ultrasonic beam to generate an electric current.

Fig. 6.1.   A car battery

6.3 Mains electricity

The electricity you use at home is an **alternating current**. The current goes through the wire first one way then the opposite way, 50 times a second. It may be useful for lighting and heating but it is no use for chemical experiments nor for most industrial chemistry. It has to be changed to a direct current by a rectifier. Also it is at a much higher voltage (240 V) than you ever need for a chemistry experiment. You may use a 'power pack' or battery charger which contains a rectifier and also a transformer so that you get direct current electricity at a suitably low voltage.

At an electric power station a fuel, usually coal, is burnt. The heat is used to boil water and make steam. The steam drives the turbines. The turbines drive the alternators which consist of magnets rotating between large coils of copper wire. Your electricity starts here in these coils and travels through a transformer to the pylon lines that weave across the country. Near your house there will be another transformer and then probably an underground cable.

Electricity may be thought of as physics, but four-fifths of our electricity starts with the chemical reaction of burning coal, oil or gas. If the water supply at a power station is of hard water this causes

Fig. 6.2. Pylon towers carrying electricity cables in the national grid. A tower is made of steel coated with zinc to prevent rusting. The cables are made of aluminium and have a steel centre for strength

a chemical problem, see Chapter 3. The water, which is needed to make steam, must be softened by using ion exchange resins.

6.4 Nuclear power

(You may find it better to read this section *after* you have read Chapter 28.)

The alchemists tried to find how to make cheap elements into gold. Modern man knows how to change one element into another by nuclear methods, but the cost of doing this is greater than the cost of the gold. Uranium is an element that is changing all the time into other elements. The change that happens is not simple radioactivity but **fission** (splitting).

Fig. 6.3.   Chapel Cross near Annan, Scotland – almost an exact copy of Calder Hall, the first nuclear power station in the world

Most uranium consists of the isotope of mass 238. A small proportion of the atoms have a mass of 235. When an atom of the 235 isotope is struck by a neutron it splits into two atoms of different elements, plus two or three neutrons, and gives off heat energy. One of the new elements has a mass of about 135 and the other a mass about 97. Both these elements are radioactive (in the usual sense) and give us the problem of radioactive waste disposal. The two or three neutrons cause other atoms of uranium-235 to undergo fission, so a chain reaction is started and a lot of energy is released.

In the UK Magnox reactors, the energy heats carbon dioxide gas which in turn heats water, and the rest of the process is the same as in a coal-burning power station. Graphite blocks are used to slow down the speed of the neutrons between the rods of uranium in their magnesium alloy cans. Rods of cadmium or boron steel are used to stop the neutrons and to shut down the chain reaction.

There are other forms of nuclear reactor but the principles are the same. Uranium is a very compact source of energy even if the proportion of uranium-235 is less than 1%. There are problems with the disposal of radioactive waste (down mines, or embedded in glass or buried in concrete in the sea?) which are not solved yet. There is the danger of an accident at a nuclear reactor or processing plant such as happened at Windscale (Sellafield, UK 1957 and 1973), Three Mile Island (USA 1979) and Chernobyl (USSR 1986). The first problem will be with us and our descendants for a long time. The second problem concerns technical faults, human error and lack of knowledge. It is here that science tails off and emotion takes over. We can choose whether to smoke, drink and drive, to take part in dangerous sports and so on, but the fear of a nuclear disaster is not diminished by 'big brother knows best'. Yet we must remem-

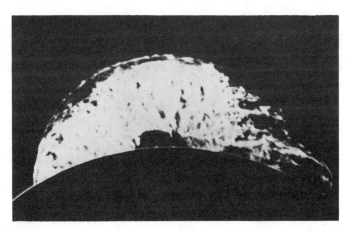

Fig. 6.4. A solar prominence – light and heat being emitted from the sun

ber that people are injured and killed in exploring and mining for coal, oil and gas.

Meanwhile research goes on into the way in which the sun generates energy, see Figure 6.4. In the sun a lot of energy is released every time four hydrogen atoms fuse together to give a helium atom. Can we do this safely on earth? If we can, there is plenty of hydrogen available in the water of the sea.

At present in the UK about a sixth (but soon a fifth) of our electricity comes from nuclear power. In France two-thirds of the electricity comes from nuclear power.

7

Recycling

7.1 Air

During the last 300 years we have burnt a large quantity of coal, oil and natural gas. The proportion of carbon dioxide in the air is increasing only very slowly in spite of this. Why is it not increasing faster? The answer is to be found in plants.

Green plants contain a magnesium compound called chlorophyll. The plants take in carbon dioxide from the air and water from their roots in the ground. The plants grow by making these compounds into sugars and at the same time they give out oxygen. This reaction takes in a lot of energy which comes from sunlight. It is called **photosynthesis**. It occurs faster in the tropics where it is warmer. The felling of tropical rain forests therefore worries many people.

When people, animals and plants respire they convert small quantities of oxygen into carbon dioxide. The quantities are small

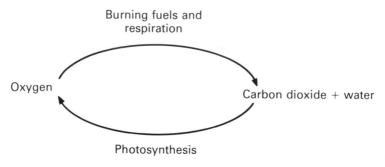

Fig. 7.1. Recycling oxygen

compared with the quantities of oxygen used in burning fuels. Even so, the Industrial Revolution has not caused us all to be asphyxiated (to die for lack of oxygen). See also Section 24.2.

7.2 Water

After air, the next most important substance to us is water. Water in a river dissolves many solids and gases. Many things get thrown into a river. We deliberately put in sewage, sometimes without thorough treatment. Some of our power stations are on rivers and they warm the water. The sea is the sink into which many things slide or are pushed. The water evaporates leaving the other materials behind and when the rain falls it is almost pure water again – to our advantage! Only a few gases are dissolved in the rainwater, see Figure 7.2.

As well as getting fish to eat from the sea it is possible that one day

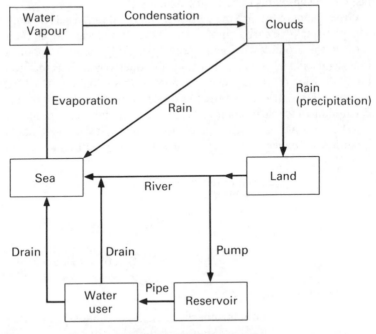

Fig. 7.2.   The water cycle

we shall dredge the sea bed for minerals. Already we drill the sea bed for oil, natural gas and sulphur.

7.3 The carbon cycle

The carbon cycle is a long-term version of the oxygen–carbon dioxide cycle in air. When carbon dioxide is converted by photosynthesis in plants, the carbon may be trapped for a long time. The plants may die and get buried or be eaten by animals. Burial and decay of plants and animals has given us our fossil fuels; coal, oil and natural gas, see Figure 7.3.

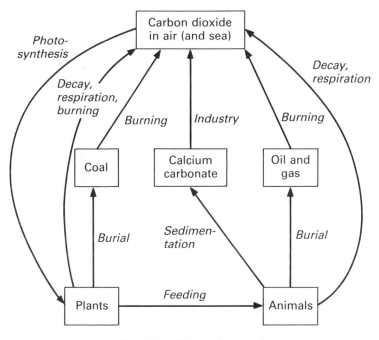

Fig. 7.3. The carbon cycle

7.4 The nitrogen cycle

Animals depend on plants because animals cannot change the nitrogen of the air into proteins nor can they convert carbon dioxide into sugars. The 'fixation' of nitrogen occurs in the nodules on the roots of leguminous plants such as peas and clover. The nodules contain colonies of bacteria. To grow enough food we have to make nitrogen into compounds and add these to the nitrogen cycle, see Figure 7.4.

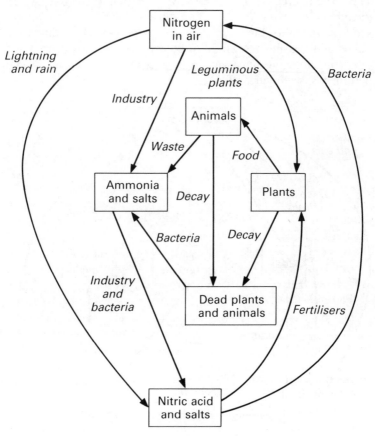

Fig. 7.4. The nitrogen cycle

7.5 Fertilisers

We now grow three-quarters of the food we need in this country. Fifty years ago we only grew one-third of what can be grown in our climate. The 'green revolution' has come, with better weedkillers, better insecticides, better varieties of seeds, more fertilisers and better preservatives for the food grown.

Three elements more than any others are important for growing crops: nitrogen, phosphorus and potassium. They are often known as NPK. If the land is to continue to be productive then these elements must be replaced in the soil after the crops have grown. Once, when mixed farming was more common, the farmer could put manure on his fields and rotate his crops to maintain the quality of the soil. Today we grow grain mostly in East Anglia and the Midlands but rear sheep and cows mostly elsewhere. Some rotation of crops occurs but not as much as before.

The **nitrogen** can be supplied as ammonia solution or even as liquid ammonia, usually piped into the soil. The most common compound used as a fertiliser is ammonium nitrate. Other compounds used are ammonium sulphate, ammonium dihydrogenphosphate, urea and calcium nitrate. Ammonium compounds are absorbed by clay and slowly released to plants. Within a week many ammonium compounds are converted into nitrates. These nitrogen compounds cause rapid growth of plants, darken the leaves and increase the yield, especially if the leaf or stem of the plant is harvested. However, nitrates are more mobile and are easily washed out of the soil by rainwater. The soil may become too acidic for plants to grow properly.

Phosphorus can be supplied to plants as calcium phosphate, which dissolves very slowly in rainwater. An alternative is a mixture called superphosphate, which contains calcium sulphate mixed with calcium dihydrogenphosphate, which is fairly soluble in water. Even blast-furnace slag may contain enough calcium phosphate to make it a useful fertiliser. Phosphorus is important for developing good roots in plants, especially when they are young.

Potassium can be supplied to plants as potassium chloride or as potassium sulphate. If you use bonfire ash you are giving your plants potassium carbonate. Potassium compounds help produce flowers and fruits, reduce the possibility of diseases and make plants hardy. If you give plants nitrogen fertilisers you increase their need for phosphorus and potassium fertilisers. The farmer tests the soil before deciding which are the right fertilisers to use.

The fertiliser bag is usually printed with the percentage of each element in it. For example, if the fertiliser is pure ammonium nitrate, the proportion of nitrogen is 35%, see Section 35.5. If this fertiliser is in a mixture then the percentage will be lower. Most of the fertilisers that are used are mixtures (compound fertilisers).

When plants rot they are oxidised and the soil becomes acidic. The best soils for crops are neutral or only very slightly acidic. So the farmer spreads calcium carbonate (lime) as a fine powder on his fields. It slowly neutralises the acids and helps break up the clay. Also it is an essential nutrient for plants, though there is rarely any shortage of it in the soil. When a gardener wants quick results he uses calcium hydroxide instead of calcium carbonate but this is not safe if there are plants in the soil.

Other major nutrients for plants include compounds of magnesium and sulphur. Minor nutrients for plants include compounds of boron, cobalt, copper, iron, manganese, molybdenum, sodium and zinc. It is rare that soils in the UK are short of these elements. If sugar beet is grown, then sodium chloride is a major nutrient not a minor one.

7.6 Pollution of the land

Have you ever thrown away a sweet paper, drink can, glass bottle, crisp packet . . . ? None of them will rot very quickly so they may be litter for a long time. If you throw away an apple core, orange peel, a lettuce leaf or a piece of stale bread, it may look bad for a short while but it will soon rot or be eaten by birds or other small creatures.

Your local authority may empty your dustbin every week but what can they do with the rubbish? They can have bottle banks and the glass can be recycled. They can collect waste paper and recycle it. Magnets can pull out the tin-plated cans and other iron objects which can go to make steel again. It is difficult to get the tin off a tin can but the problem has been solved. Two plants are under construction in the UK to do this. Many drinks cans are made of aluminium so they will have to be hand-picked out of the rubbish. A lot of the rubbish can be burnt to give energy which can make water into steam to drive a turbine and make electricity, see Figure 7.5.

The burning of plastics is not always safe. One common one, PVC, gives off fumes of the poisonous gas hydrogen chloride when

Fig. 7.5. Edmonton power station where some of London's rubbish is burnt and electricity made

it is burnt. The plastics used in furniture now are even more dangerous when burnt but safer ones are being developed.

There is a danger that things we use or throw away can get into food chains and poison other creatures. The insecticide DDT was used widely until it was realised that it caused birds to become infertile or to lay eggs with such thin shells that they were easily broken. Lead weights were often used by anglers but they caused swans to die of lead poisoning. There are many compounds used in industry and in agriculture which are known to be poisonous or which may have damaging effects that we will only discover in 10 or 20 years' time. We must be on our guard at all times.

7.7 Recycling metals

The supplies of calcium carbonate and sodium chloride are so large that we do not worry about them running out. However, the two metals that we use most, iron and aluminium, are recycled when-ever possible. Most of the ores for making these metals have to be imported into the UK. A lot of scrap iron is available from old cars, fridges, washing machines and buildings. The scrap iron can be used straight away in the steel-making process, avoiding the cost of the blast-furnace process to make the iron. If scrap aluminium is recycled, the expense of the electrical process and the need for a supply of carbon (graphite) and bauxite ore are eliminated: the scrap is just checked for impurities, then melted. Many other metals are in even shorter supply than iron and aluminium, and the recycling of tin, lead, zinc, nickel and copper scrap is important.

(The problems of the finite (limited) supply of the fossil fuels and hence the need for alternative sources of energy have been dis-cussed in Chapter 5.)

7.8 Corrosion

A lot of time and money is spent in getting metals. The problem then is that the metals corrode. They react with the oxygen and carbon dioxide in the air and with water: they tend to go back to their original compounds.

(*a*) Potassium and sodium must be kept under oil (naphtha) to prevent them reacting completely.

(*b*) Calcium can be kept in a bottle but it tends to go white in air because it gets a thin layer of calcium carbonate on its surface. With water it would react completely.

(*c*) Magnesium slowly gets a thin layer of magnesium oxide and magnesium carbonate on its surface.

(*d*) Aluminium slowly gets a thin layer of aluminium oxide on its surface and this layer sticks firmly, protecting the metal under-neath. This layer is often put on deliberately in a process called anodising.

(*e*) Zinc slowly gets a thin layer of zinc oxide and zinc carbonate on its surface.

(*f*) Iron forms rust in moist air, see Section 7.9. The word 'rusting' is used only for the corrosion of iron.

(*g*) Lead and copper very slowly get a thin layer of their com-pounds, mainly carbonates, on their surfaces.

(*h*) Gold and platinum are often used in jewellery because it is rare for them to tarnish. Silver is also used but may go black in town air; silver cutlery is blackened by eggs and Brussels sprouts. Sulphur compounds in the air or food react with silver to form black silver sulphide.

7.9 Rusting

More iron is used for making things than all the other metals put together. Air and water are both necessary for its corrosion. The oxygen of the air and liquid water (not just water vapour) together cause iron to form rust. The rusting is faster if there are substances such as salt dissolved in the water. Salt and grit may be put on the roads in winter to help remove ice and snow but they cause a lot of damage to bridges, cars and lorries. It is not wise to park your car on the seafront, especially when the wind blows in from the sea.

The brown compound known as rust is hydrated iron(III) oxide. Rust is porous and flakes off a surface, so more of the iron is exposed to the air and water and rusts. Most other metals when they corrode form a thin layer of compounds that stick firmly to the surface and so protect the remaining metal.

There are many ways of trying to prevent rusting. Many of these depend on trying to keep out air and/or water. A lot of money could be saved if rusting could be prevented or slowed down.

(*a*) Parts of a car or a bicycle can be painted. On moving parts that cannot be painted you can put oil or grease. (How effective would painting a bicycle chain be?)

(*b*) A thin layer of a more reactive metal can be put on the iron. Zinc is used for this purpose. The process is called **galvanising**; it is often done by electricity. (Who was Galvani, and what famous experiment did he do?) If the film of zinc is scratched, exposing the iron, it is still the zinc that corrodes rather than the iron. Corrugated iron is galvanised before it is used for buildings, dustbins, etc. Aluminium paint is used in a similar way.

(*c*) A lump of a more reactive metal can be put in contact with the iron. Magnesium and zinc are used to protect ships, pipelines and tanks in this way, see Figure 7.6.

(*d*) A thin layer of a less reactive metal can be put on the iron. Items such as taps, and bicycle and car parts are often nickel plated before they are chromium plated. For foods, tin-plated steel cans ('tin cans') must be used because tin is the only metal that forms non-poisonous compounds when the acids in food slowly attack it. The disadvantage is that if the film of the less reactive metal is pierced then the iron underneath corrodes rapidly.

Fig. 7.6.   Strips of zinc are bolted on to the side of a ship to try to prevent rusting

Instead of trying to prevent rusting of iron there is another way of tackling the problem: use alternative materials. Instead of using iron (or mild steel) you can use stainless steel. Stainless steel does not rust because a very thin film of chromium(III) oxide sticks firmly to its surface. You will find stainless steel used for cutlery, sinks, teapots, car exhausts and many other things. Another alternative is to use another metal or a plastic. What are the advantages and disadvantages of a plastic bucket compared with a steel bucket?

8

Changes

8.1 Experiments

If you do an experiment you are trying out an idea. Sometimes your guess at the result turns out to be correct, sometimes not. The more experience you have the better you may be at forecasting the result. You can put related results together and call the pattern or general statement of them a **law**. You may try to explain how the results happen and call your idea a **hypothesis**. After more experiments in which you guess the results correctly, because you have found a consistent pattern in the results, you may call your results a chemical or scientific law and your explanation a **theory**. After a while you may do experiments that your theory cannot explain, and so a better theory which is not so limited as the first one is needed.

When the substances change in an experiment you may call the ones you start with **reagents** or **reactants**. The substances you finish with are often called **products**. For example, you can try putting washing soda crystals into vinegar. The vinegar has a well-known smell. When you put the crystals into the vinegar there is a fizz as a gas escapes: it is carbon dioxide. The solution you are left with does not smell if you use enough washing soda crystals. You can boil the solution that is left or you can leave it out for a long time for water to evaporate. Then you get some crystals which will not fizz if put into vinegar. You have made a new substance. You have caused a **chemical change** (a **reaction**). The washing soda and the vinegar are the reagents. The carbon dioxide, the new crystals (sodium ethanoate) and some water (unseen) are the products.

The burning of fuels, the corrosion of metals and the rusting of iron are all chemical changes.

If you put washing soda or salt crystals in water, they dissolve. If you boil the solution for a few minutes and then let it cool you will get back your crystals of washing soda or salt. A solution is a mixture, see Chapter 13. The changes of making a solution (dissolution) and of getting the crystals back again (crystallisation) are called **physical changes** because no new substances are made.

The opposite result can also occur: substances do not always mix, let alone react. If you put oil on water it floats: no mixing or reaction occurs. Oil and water are said to be **immiscible**.

In a chemistry laboratory, a place for doing experiments, you will find many bottles of reagents. Some experiments are safe, others might be dangerous. Don't do things unless you are told to. It is the same at home: children have to learn that knives may be sharp, that the stove may be hot, that you can't breathe under water . . . In a laboratory, there may be poisonous substances, so don't try tasting them and don't suck your fingers or pens. Remember to wash your hands after doing experiments.

8.2 More about physical changes

You can mix salt and water. The salt breaks up into such tiny pieces that you can't see them, even with a microscope. The salt dissolves in the water making salt **solution**. We call the salt the **solute** and the water the **solvent**, see Chapter 13.

$$solute + solvent \rightarrow solution$$

If you leave the salt solution out in a room for several days you will get the salt crystals back again. The water has evaporated: the water has become a gas and mixed with the air. Evaporation can occur at any temperature. You can speed up crystallisation by heating the solution and then letting it cool. The same experiment can be done with sugar. You don't get back all of the crystals unless you let all of the water evaporate.

When you dissolve the crystals of salt in water you may notice that the solution is slightly colder than the water was. You can try using a thermometer to measure the temperature before and after. Physical changes such as this often occur with small energy changes.

Measuring the temperature is a way of measuring heat energy changes.

If you heat some crystals of salt in a test tube they remain colourless crystals even if they become a little smaller. With a very hot flame it is possible to melt salt. Melted salt when cooled goes back to solid salt. It is like ice melting to give water when heat from a room or better weather affects it. If you put the water back in the fridge or there is another frost, the water forms ice again.

Ice and water are the same substance. Solid salt and melted salt are the same substance. Ice will do many of the same things as cold water – in a drink of squash, for example. Solid salt and melted salt are still the same compound, sodium chloride. So physical changes do not change substances into other substances. Figure 8.1 shows some of the differences between physical changes and chemical changes.

	Physical change	*Chemical change*
Substances	stay the same	new ones formed
Easy to reverse?	yes	no
Heat (energy) change	small	large
Solvents	stay the same	new ones needed
Chemical behaviour	no different	very different

Fig. 8.1.   Physical and chemical changes

Try to decide if the following are physical changes:

(*a*) changing water into steam;
(*b*) making milk into cheese;
(*c*) dissolving sugar in a cup of tea;
(*d*) letting jelly set;
(*e*) baking a sponge cake.

(Answers on page 267.)

8.3 More about chemical changes

You can heat sugar in a test tube. You can smell the caramel you make. This is a chemical change. It is hard, if not impossible, to reverse. Have you ever heard of making toast into bread? The colours of sugar and caramel, of bread and toast are different. Not only do they look different but they taste different. Chemical changes give us new substances.

The properties that we study may be:

physical properties – colour
melting point
boiling point
density
solubility . . .
or chemical properties – changes on heating
reactions with other substances such as air, water, acids, alkalis . . .

We use the properties of substances to identify them or to know whether a chemical change has occurred. Sometimes to identify a substance you have to take drastic action and pull it to pieces. Identifying a substance in this way is called **analysing** it. The opposite is **synthesising** a substance – putting it together, usually from its elements.

Try pouring hydrochloric acid into sodium hydroxide solution (take care – this is a corrosive alkali). Feel the outside of the vessel and notice that it gets hot. A chemical change has occurred and heat (energy) is given out. Chemical changes usually occur together with large heat changes. When you have neutralised an acid with an alkali you get a salt plus water; you have made new substances:

$$\text{acid} + \text{alkali} \rightarrow \text{salt} + \text{water}$$

For example:

hydrochloric acid + sodium hydroxide → sodium chloride
+ water

It is hard but not impossible to reverse this change. (You have to use electricity, see Chapter 14.)

To cause some chemical changes you have to heat the reagents. Then it is harder to find out how much heat is given out when the reaction happens – was it more heat than was needed to cause the reaction, or the same amount of heat, or less?

Try to decide if the following are chemical changes:

(*a*) letting an iron nail rust;
(*b*) magnetising an iron nail;
(*c*) growing a plant;
(*d*) using petrol in a car engine;
(*e*) snapping a piece of wood.

(Answers on page 267.)

9

Solids, Liquids and Gases

9.1 Cold, warm and hot

When things are 'cold' they are often solids, for example ice, candle wax, iron and salt. When you warm them they melt, some easily, some with difficulty. Then you have the liquid substance. Melting (or fusing) is a physical change: its opposite is solidifying (or freezing). The melting point of a single or *pure* solid is a very important fact. When a substance is pure it has a definite, constant melting temperature, see Figure 9.1. If it is not pure its melting temperature is often lower than usual and is not so definite – it melts over a range of temperature. The melting point of ice, also the freezing point of water, is 0 °C. If salt is dissolved in water the freezing point is below 0 °C. This is why salt is put on icy roads in winter.

When things are 'warm' they are often liquids, for example water, ethanol ('alcohol') and propanone (acetone, nail varnish remover). If you cool them they will freeze. If you heat them they will boil; then you have the gaseous substance. Boiling is a physical change; its opposite is condensing. The boiling point of a *pure* liquid is a very important fact. When a substance is pure it has a definite, constant boiling temperature, see Figure 9.1. If it is not pure its boiling temperature is often higher than usual and is not so definite.

A boiling point is affected by the pressure of the air around us. The normal boiling point of water is 100 °C. At the top of Mount Everest water will boil at 72 °C because the pressure is lower. Inside a pressure cooker, where the pressure is twice the normal pressure, the boiling point of water is 121 °C – so food cooks faster. If you put salt in water the boiling point is more than 100 °C but the temperature of the steam above the water will be exactly 100 °C.

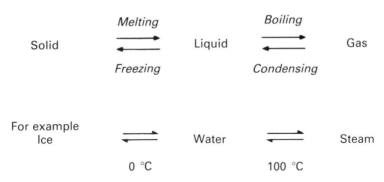

Fig. 9.1. Heating and cooling a substance

When things are 'hot' they are often gases, for example steam, methane and air (nitrogen, oxygen, argon, carbon dioxide . . .). If you cool a gas it will condense – for some gases this is easy to do but for others it is difficult. The volume and/or pressure of a gas increase as the temperature increases. If the temperature of a gas is kept constant, then if the pressure goes up the volume goes down.

Cold, warm and hot are relative terms. For some substances 'cold' is very cold indeed – they are nearly always gases. For other substances 'hot' is very hot indeed – they are nearly always solids. We measure temperatures on the Celsius (centigrade) scale. The lowest temperature that anything can get to is −273 °C, also called zero kelvin (0 K) or absolute zero.

9.2 The three states of matter

Solids, liquids and gases are called the three **states of matter**. Most substances can exist in all three states. The melting and boiling points of some substances are given in Figure 9.2. Notice that the two temperatures are equal for carbon dioxide. When solid carbon dioxide gets warmer it changes straight away into a gas: it **sublimes**. If the gas touches anything which is very cold it changes straight back into a solid. Carbon dioxide is used as 'dry ice' to keep things cold – there is no messy liquid when it has done its job.

Substance	Melting point/°C	Boiling point/°C
Hydrogen	−259	−253
Oxygen	−219	−183
Methane	−182	−161
Ethanol	−114	78
Propanone	−95	56
Carbon dioxide	−78	−78
Aluminium	660	2450
Sodium chloride	801	1470
Copper	1083	2600
Iron	1535	2900

Fig. 9.2. The melting and boiling points of some common substances

When a solid is in lots of very small pieces it is called a **powder**. If a solid consists of pieces with a definite shape it is said to be **crystalline**, see Section 32.1. The abbreviations

s   for solid
l   for liquid
g   for gas
aq for a solution in water

are useful for describing the state in which a substance exists.

Figure 9.3 gives a general summary of the properties of the three states of matter. Water is an exception to these general properties. Between 0 °C and 4 °C its density is greater than that of ice and *increases* on heating. Above 4 °C the density of water decreases on heating, which is usual for a liquid being heated.

9.3 The kinetic theory

What are solids, liquids and gases made of? The answer is: lots of tiny particles moving about. Kinetic energy is energy of movement: the faster or the heavier the particle, the greater the kinetic energy. We cannot see the individual particles but we can detect them by colour changes and in other ways.

If you put a drop of liquid bromine (careful, very corrosive) at the bottom of a jar of air, then before long you see red-brown

Property	Solid	Liquid	Gas
Shape	obvious – may be crystalline	same as that of container – may be spherical if on its own	can be any – it fills its container
Volume	definite	definite	depends a lot on pressure and temperature
Density	high	medium	very low
Will it flow?	only if in small pieces	easily	very easily
Can you compress it?	no	no	yes
Does it expand on heating?	not much	not much	a lot

Fig. 9.3. The general properties of solids, liquids and gases

fumes travelling all around the jar. The spreading out is called **diffusion**.

If you put one crystal of potassium manganate(VII) at the bottom of a beaker of water then after a few minutes you see the purple colour spreading out. The higher the temperature of the water, the faster the diffusion. If you have a lot of patience you can look at intervals at a large crystal of copper(II) sulphate gradually dissolving in water in a tall jar over a period of a week.

A fourth experiment is to put two cottonwool pads, one soaked in concentrated hydrochloric acid and the other in concentrated aqueous ammonia, at opposite ends of a horizontal glass tube. Where the gases from these two solutions meet you get a white ring of solid. Look carefully where the ring forms and then you can work out which particles travelled faster.

In solids the particles are touching one another and all they can do is vibrate. We know that some solids have a smell, so occasionally some particles must escape to form a gas. In a crystalline solid the particles are arranged in a regular pattern, see Chapter 32 and Figure 9.4.

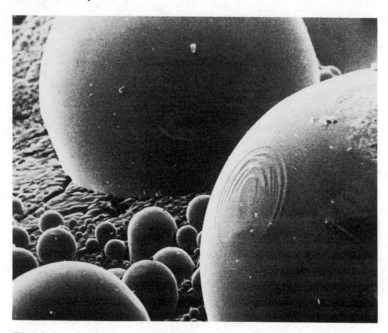

Fig. 9.4. A picture of the surface of a solid taken with a special
microscope

In a liquid the particles are usually touching one another but they
are not in a fixed or regular pattern. They can move at random (see
the potassium manganate(VII) experiment above) or they can
move all together when they are poured from one beaker to
another. Liquids (and solids) cannot be compressed – the hydraulic
jack used at the garage to raise your car depends on this fact. In
liquids a few more particles can escape, so liquids are more likely to
have a smell than solids.

In a gas the particles are moving very fast. A gas can be compressed, so there must be a lot of space between the particles at
ordinary pressure. This is so even in the tyres of your bicycle,
otherwise you would feel every small stone you run over.

The quick random movement of particles in liquids and gases
means that it is much easier to mix them than to separate them. Pour
water into orange squash: how do you get the water back again?

Open a bottle of perfume: how do you get the perfume back into the bottle?

You can use a microscope to see some examples of **Brownian motion**. This is the random zig-zag motion of the particles you can see caused by uneven bombardment with tiny particles that you cannot see. Pollen or carbon (graphite) in water can be used for the experiment. A smoke box gives the same result; in this case carbon (soot) particles are being bombarded by air particles.

10

Elements and Compounds

10.1 Aluminium atoms

Take a piece of aluminium cooking foil (1 cm × 1 cm) and a pair of scissors. Cut the piece of foil in half. It is still aluminium – you can tell that by its properties (appearance, feel . . .). Cut it in half again. It's still aluminium. How often can you cut it in half? Do you stop it being aluminium? Cutting is a physical change, but it is difficult to reverse it without melting the aluminium. You could carry on and on using the scissors under a microscope. The most powerful microscope in a university is not good enough to let you see the smallest particle of aluminium, the atom.

Atoms are very, very tiny. In the smallest piece of aluminium you can cut, there are millions and millions and millions of atoms. Dalton emphasised the importance of the mass of atoms, see Section 10.4. All the experiments you can do with aluminium involve complete atoms or their ions, see Chapters 14, 28 and 30.

An element is a substance which cannot be decomposed (split up) into two or more different substances by chemical experiments.

An atom is the smallest particle of an element that can exist and take part in chemical reactions.

Besides aluminium there are about 100 other elements known. Most of them occur naturally but a few of them are man-made. Two hundred years ago only about 30 elements were known. People looked for patterns in the properties of the elements and tried to explain the results they found, see Chapter 29.

10.2 Law of conservation of mass

This is one of the two laws which Dalton used to work out his atomic theory. If you weigh substance A with substance B before a reaction, let the reaction occur and then weigh the substance C which has been made, you get the same answer. This law may seem obvious and true, but a hundred years after Dalton, further experiments were done which showed that the law was not perfect. Still, it is true in your experiments, and it is important because it made scientists think about chemical theory.

The easiest experiments to do in the laboratory to prove this law are experiments using two solutions. The solutions must react to cause a colour change or give a solid substance which is insoluble, so that it settles out (a **precipitate**). It is not a good idea to choose an experiment in which a gas is formed in case the cork flies off the apparatus. A suitable pair of solutions is iodine and starch. Iodine solution is brown and starch solution is white. When they mix there is a colour change (find it out). This is the way you can test food to see if it contains starch.

The apparatus can be set up as in Figure 10.1: weigh it, tip it to mix the solutions and start the reaction, then reweigh it. Another pair of solutions you can try is copper(II) sulphate and sodium carbonate.

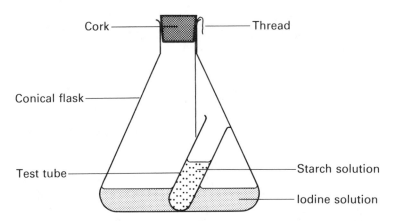

Fig. 10.1. An apparatus to demonstrate the law of conservation of mass

In a chemical reaction, the total mass at the start is equal to the total mass at the end.

10.3 Law of constant composition

This is the second law which gave Dalton his ideas. Again it may seem obvious, but scientists like proof – they don't believe you unless you can show them, not just tell them. If you get samples of a compound from all over the world then they are all made up in the same way. The same compound is made from the same elements in the same proportions each time. Instead of trying to get them from all over the world you can make the samples in different ways in the laboratory.

If you heat a piece of copper foil in air it changes from brown to black. Scratch the surface and you find that it is still brown underneath. The black substance is copper(II) oxide: the oxygen has come from the air. The reaction has not converted all the copper to copper(II) oxide so other routes have to be found to make copper(II) oxide more efficiently. The reaction scheme shown in Figure 10.2 gives you four routes to get copper oxide. Substances like sodium hydroxide and nitric acid are corrosive, so you have to be careful (acids are nearly always dilute solutions in experiments, see Chapter 21).

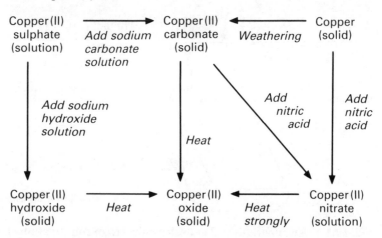

Fig. 10.2.   Routes to black copper(II) oxide

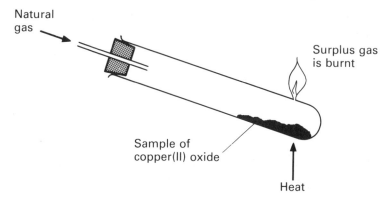

Fig. 10.3. An apparatus to demonstrate the law of constant composition

The second stage is to analyse the samples of copper(II) oxide you have made, see Figure 10.3. You heat them in a stream of natural gas: turn on the gas and, after a pause to let air be pushed out of the tube, light the gas. Heat the tube very strongly from underneath with a Bunsen burner. Turn off the Bunsen burner and let the copper that has been produced cool while natural gas is still passing through the tube. The reason for this is that air must not get at the hot copper. It would turn it back, at least on the surface, to copper(II) oxide. Finally weigh the cold copper. You can show that the same mass of copper(II) oxide always contains the same mass of copper. You know a chemical reaction has occurred by the colour change.

All pure samples of the same chemical compound contain the same elements joined together in the same proportions by mass.

10.4 Dalton's atomic theory

Dalton (Figure 10.4) was not the first or the last person to talk about atoms. People before Dalton did not do experiments or think about what they saw carefully enough. Dalton based his ideas on the study of gases and on the law of conservation of mass and the law of constant composition. Dalton's ideas (his theory) can be written like this.

(*a*) Substances are made up of a large number of atoms which are very tiny particles. You cannot split up, destroy or make atoms.

(*b*) All the atoms of one element are the same in all ways. You know which element is which by the mass of the atoms. Different elements have atoms of different masses.

(*c*) In a simple chemical reaction (that of synthesis), one or more atoms of one element combine with one or more atoms of a second element to give a molecule of a compound.

Fig. 10.4.   John Dalton, 1766–1844, England. The brains behind the atomic theory

When you make a compound you find that you have a substance with new properties. It does not have the properties of the two or more elements with which you started. For example, aluminium powder will burn in air, combining with the oxygen. Aluminium is a grey solid, oxygen is a colourless gas. Their melting points, boiling points, densities and chemical properties are different. They are different elements. Put them together to make aluminium oxide and you have a compound with a new melting point, boiling point, etc. Aluminium oxide is a white powder but it can be made into colourless crystals which are very hard: they are used as the 'jewels' in clockwork watches, and as abrasives.

A compound is a substance which contains two or more elements joined together in such way that their properties are changed.

A molecule is the smallest particle of an element or a compound which can exist on its own.

Dalton's atomic theory has been replaced by the modern atomic theory, see Chapter 28. However, his theory still applies to most of the chemistry that happens inside you, that you can do in the laboratory and that we do in industry. Today we identify an element by its atomic number and we take the average mass of its atoms as typical of that element. The word molecule is not used when we want to emphasise that the bonding in a compound is ionic, see Chapter 30.

10.5 Naming compounds

To name a compound containing a metal plus a non-metal, the metal is put first and the non-metal second, see Chapter 11. The end of the name of the non-metal is changed to -**ide** to show that it is in a compound. For example:

sodium	+	chlorine	→	sodium chloride
aluminium	+	oxygen	→	aluminium oxide
iron	+	sulphur	→	iron sulphide
potassium	+	iodine	→	potassium iodide

There are some very common compounds which have names that do not tell you what is in them:

water is hydrogen oxide
ammonia is nitrogen hydride
methane is carbon hydride

The only other compounds whose names end in -**ide** are the hydroxides, which contain hydrogen and oxygen as well as the metal. For example, sodium hydroxide is sodium, hydrogen and oxygen.

If two metals are put together they do not make a compound, they form a mixture known as an **alloy**. If two non-metals make a compound then to name the compound you write the most non-metallic element second, see Chapter 11.

Many compounds consist of three elements: a metal and two

non-metals. If the second non-metal is oxygen, the name ends in
-**ate**. For example:

copper carbonate is copper, carbon and oxygen
sodium nitrate is sodium, nitrogen and oxygen
calcium sulphate is calcium, sulphur and oxygen.

10.6 Mixtures

Substances do not always join together when you put them
together, even if you heat them. They sometimes form mixtures.
You and I, and the world around us, are mixtures of compounds and
elements. The properties of mixtures are the properties of all the
parts put together. For example, if you mix carbon and chalk
powders, the colour may range from black to grey to white: it
depends on the proportions.

A solution is a mixture. Salt can be dissolved in water. If you boil
the solution you can get the salt crystals back again (by evaporation
and crystallisation). Physical processes can be used to separate a
mixture as well as to make one. Chapter 12 talks about ways of
separating mixtures.

You cannot tell by looking if there is salt dissolved in water so you
have to do experiments. You will find that the freezing point is now
below 0 °C and the boiling point is now above 100 °C. The density
(often given as the mass of 1 ml) is changed. If you are absolutely
sure that you have mixed common salt (sodium chloride) and water
in a perfectly clean dish, then tasting it would be safe to prove it.
Chemical changes can also be used to show that there is salt in the
water, see Chapter 38.

11

Metals and Non-metals

11.1 Metals

In history we learn about the Bronze Age and the Iron Age. Possibly before the Bronze Age there was the Copper Age. Each age advanced by making use of a new material because its properties were better than those of the old materials. Why are copper, bronze and iron better than wood and stone? They are stronger and do not break so easily. After melting they can be cast into useful shapes. They can be beaten into thin sheets (they are malleable). It is rare to get a musical note from a stone but you can have a steel drum band. Later on it was discovered that metals would conduct an electric current. You could not have electricity in your home without wires. Wires made of metals can also be used to build suspension bridges, see Figure 11.1. Some general properties of metals are given in Figure 11.2.

11.2 Non-metals

Many non-metals are gases at room temperature. This means that their melting and boiling points are much lower than those of metals. Non-metals are fewer than metals and you may find it harder to recognise them as a set of elements. Some non-metals are oxygen, nitrogen, chlorine and argon. In their properties the non-metals are the opposite of metals: they do not conduct electricity, you cannot make them into wires (they are not ductile) or sheets (they are not malleable), they are not very strong even when solidified (they are brittle). Some general properties of non-metals are given in Figure 11.2.

Fig. 11.1.   The suspension bridge over the River Humber at Hull

Property	Metals	Non-metals
Melting point	high	low
Boiling point	high	low
State	usually solids	often gases
Density	high	low
Conductivity of heat and electricity	high	low
Ductile?	yes	no
Strength	high	low
Hardness	high	low
Malleable?	yes and they are sonorous	no, they are brittle
Colour	grey	many colourless
Shininess (lustre)	bright	dull

Fig. 11.2.   Some general properties of metals and non-metals

11.3 Semi-metals

It is easy to classify the squares on a chess board: black and white. It is not so easy to classify changes or substances in the world around us. Physical and chemical changes are easy to distinguish in some experiments but the division becomes harder as the range of experiments becomes wider.

It may be easy to classify some elements as metals or non-metals. But here are some exceptions to the general properties given in Figure 11.2.

mercury is a metal but it is a liquid at room temperature;

sodium, tin and some other metals have low melting points;

copper and gold are not grey (silver-coloured) like most metals;

carbon in the form of graphite is usually considered as a non-metal but it conducts electricity;

carbon in the form of diamond is usually considered as a non-metal but it is harder than all metals;

carbon in both these crystalline forms (called allotropes, see Section 32.4) and silicon have melting points higher than many metals;

iodine is a non-metal but it is denser than many metals;

bromine is the only liquid non-metal at room temperature.

Some of the elements that are hard to classify are called **semi-metals**; silicon is typical of them. This borderline position of silicon is important because it is the element we use in calculators and computers. If electricity at a very low voltage is applied to silicon it is a non-conductor. If you increase the voltage then it *will* conduct. Silicon is called a **semiconductor**. By adding another element to some silicon ('doping' it) and then putting it next to a wafer of pure silicon you have a device which will conduct an electric current better in one direction than another: a diode.

12

Separating a Mixture

12.1 Ways to do it

A mixture can have any composition. It is important to be able to separate it into pure substances so that you can study their properties. Later you can make a mixture of known proportions of each substance and study its properties.

Many of the ways of separating a mixture involve physical changes. The substances are not changed during the experiment. There are some mixtures which can be separated only by chemically changing the substances as they are being separated. These chemical changes may be quite complicated.

12.2 Melting

It is rare to be able to melt a solid mixture to obtain a pure substance. If you had a mixture of candle wax and sand you could warm it until the wax melted. When you tried to pour off the wax (to decant it) it would probably still carry some sand with it. However, sulphur is extracted from some rocks by melting it, as in the Frasch process, see Section 17.6. This is done in the USA and Poland where the sulphur is found underground.

12.3 Boiling

If you boil some tap water in a kettle the substances dissolved in the water usually remain in the kettle and steam escapes. If you can safely hold a cold plate or piece of glass near the spout then you will see that the steam turns back into water. It is now pure water, often called distilled water. In the laboratory this can be done by heating the water in a flask attached to a water-cooled condenser (a Liebig condenser), see Figure 12.1. If you put some anti-bumping granules in the water it will boil smoothly.

This process, called **distillation**, can be used also to separate a mixture of two or more liquids, if their boiling points are reasonably far apart. In this way liquid air can be separated into oxygen, nitrogen and other gases, see Section 1.2. Crude oil can be separated into petrol, paraffin and other substances, see Section 5.3. For these purposes a long column is put above the boiling mixture and the separation continues up the column (fractional distillation). When whisky is being made, the mixture of alcohol and water is distilled to increase the proportion of alcohol in the water, see Figure 19.1.

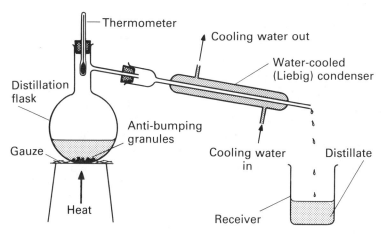

Fig. 12.1. An apparatus for distillation

12.4 Cooling

If you have a concentrated solution of salt in water and cool it, then you will get crystals of salt. You can speed up this process by warming the solution first, to boil off some of the water. As the warm concentrated solution cools, the crystals of salt will form quickly. Boiling off *all* the water will cause any impurities that are with the salt and water to crystallise as well. If you are prepared to wait for a long time for the crystals of salt to form, you can let evaporation occur at room temperature.

If you have a *very dilute* solution of salt in water and you cool it, then you will get crystals of pure ice. This will leave the salt in solution.

12.5 Filtering

River water is often muddy. There are particles of soil floating around in the water. The soil is in **suspension** in the water. It has not dissolved: the particles can still be seen. If the water is left standing in a reservoir the soil settles. This is part of the process used to get drinking water.

When I am filling the petrol tank on my lawn mower I use a funnel with some wire gauze in it. The gauze filters out any grass blowing around and stops it getting into the engine. You can filter river water too, but gauze is not good enough. You have to use filter paper which has very small invisible holes in it. The water can pass through but the soil remains on the paper. You fold the circle of filter paper into quarters and then open it, three layers on one side and one on the other, see Figure 12.2. The paper in the funnel should not be filled to the top because particles of soil may escape round it. The liquid passing through the filter paper is called the **filtrate**. The solid remaining on the paper is called the **residue**, see Figure 12.3.

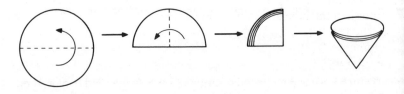

Fig. 12.2.   Fold a piece of filter paper into quarters, then open it as shown

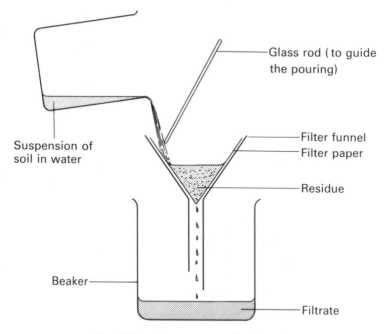

Fig. 12.3. An apparatus for filtration

12.6 Centrifuging

Your washing machine at home may separate the water from the clothes by spinning the drum. The water can pass through the holes in the drum but the clothes cannot. You are centrifuging the water from the clothes and the drum acts as a filter. The difference between the laboratory centrifuge and your washing machine is that the test tube does not have holes in it, so the solids remain in the bottom of the tube under the liquid.

The test tube full of the suspension must be counterbalanced by another test tube full of water on the opposite arm of the centrifuge, see Figure 12.4. Keep your fingers out because the rotor in the centrifuge goes very fast. When you have spun the tubes for a minute or two and let the centrifuge stop, you will find that the suspension has become the residue at the bottom of the tube. Now you can decant off the liquid from above the residue.

Fig. 12.4.   A centrifuge

12.7 Dissolving

If you have a mixture of two substances, one soluble in water and the other not, it is easy to separate the two. A list of soluble compounds is given in Section 13.3. For example, you can shake a mixture of sodium carbonate (washing soda) and calcium carbonate (chalk) with water: sodium carbonate dissolves, calcium carbonate remains as a suspension. Filter or centrifuge and you have the calcium carbonate there immediately. Evaporate the filtrate and you get back the crystals of sodium carbonate.

You don't have to use water as the solvent. A useful solvent is ethanol (alcohol) which is used for many perfumes that are not soluble in water. Another useful solvent is propanone (acetone): it is sold as nail varnish remover. Liquid Paper and some dry cleaning fluids use 1,1,1-trichloroethane as the solvent.

12.8 Paper chromatography I

If you spill some blackcurrant juice on the tablecloth you will see it spread out in a circular way like the ripples on a pond when you drop in a stone. You can use the idea of a substance spreading out from the centre to separate a mixture or to check if a substance is pure.

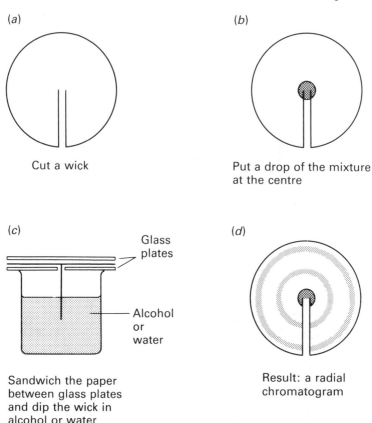

Fig. 12.5. Separating a mixture by radial chromatography

Cut a wick from the edge to the centre of a piece of filter paper. Fold the wick down at right angles and put a drop of black ink at the centre of the paper, see Figure 12.5 (a) and (b). Sandwich the filter paper between two glass plates for the best results, see Figure

12.5(c). The bottom plate has a hole in it and the wick dips into a beaker of ethanol or water underneath. You will see the ethanol creep up the wick and separate the ink into several coloured circles. The black ink is probably a mixture of several coloured substances, see Figure 12.5(d). This experiment is an example of radial chromatography.

The different coloured substances in the black ink have different solubilities in the moving solvent so they move at different speeds outwards on the paper.

12.9 Paper chromatography II

Paper chromatography can be done in another way. Put a spot of a solution of the substance to be analysed near the bottom of a square piece of filter paper. Stand the paper in a beaker containing a shallow layer of ethanol or water. The ethanol must creep up the paper to reach the spot of the mixture. Cover the beaker with a lid to prevent too much loss by evaporation. After a while you will find a set of spots in a line up the paper. Each spot corresponds to a ring in the previous method, see Figure 12.6. Don't let the ethanol reach the top of the paper. The paper can be coiled into a cylinder but you will not get a good result if the paper touches the side of the beaker, or if the coil overlaps too much. Here you have made an **ascending chromatogram**.

Chromatography is one way in which your local authority can check that the food you eat contains only approved colouring substances. Doctors use chromatography to analyse urine to study if your body is working properly. It is one of the techniques forensic scientists use to help solve crimes.

If you want to know if particular known substances are present in your unknown mixture, you can put spots of the known substances beside the spot of mixture on the paper. If one of the spots produced from the mixture is at the same height as the spot produced by one of the known substances, then you know that the mixture contains that substance.

(a)

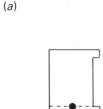

Put a spot of the mixture
near the bottom edge of
the paper and cut away
part of one edge.

(b)

Curl the paper into a cylinder.
Clip it and stand it in a
shallow layer of alcohol or water.
Cover the beaker with a lid.

(c)

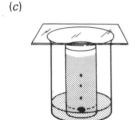

Stop the experiment when
the alcohol or water gets
near the top of the paper.

(d)

An improved way of starting
the experiment is to put
known substances by the
side of the spot of mixture.
This mixture contains substances
a, c and d.

Fig. 12.6. Separating a mixture by ascending chromatography

12.10 Magnetising

When we throw away our rubbish, sensible local authorities try to
get out the valuable parts. Iron is attracted by a magnet so that scrap
iron can be separated from other metals, paper, plastic and so on.
Mixtures of metals that contain a lot of iron (ferrous scrap) are also
separated. You can try separating a mixture of iron filings and
sulphur powder by using a magnet. Notice that some sulphur
powder may cling to the filings so the separation is not perfect.

12.11 Floating

An iceberg floats because ice is less dense than water. However, the ability to float does not always depend on density. A very fine powder will often float on water even if you find that a lump of the substance will sink. There is a peculiar property of liquid surfaces, especially water, called 'surface tension'. Watch a water boatman insect on the surface of a pond. Then try floating aluminium foil on water (aluminium is denser than water).

The extraction of copper, lead and many other metals starts with mining rocks which contain their compounds. The rocks are ground to a powder and then put in tanks of water. Air is bubbled into the tanks and metal compounds rise to the surface leaving the soil at the bottom. Small quantities of other substances are added to improve the efficiency of the process.

12.12 Absorption

Concentrated calcium chloride solution will absorb moisture (water) from the air. Air is a mixture of gases and the water vapour can be removed in this way. Many simple gases can be dried similarly, for example oxygen, nitrogen, hydrogen and carbon dioxide. Another, more dangerous, drying agent is concentrated sulphuric acid.

Wood charcoal is a very porous form of carbon: it is like a sponge. It can be used to absorb bromine out of air. You can see the red-brown coloured gas disappearing as it sticks to the surface or penetrates into the charcoal. This is how a dry-cleaning shop keeps the valuable solvent 'perc' from escaping into the air around it and how some cooker hoods keep the kitchen free of smells.

An easy experiment to do in the laboratory is to use animal charcoal to take a dye called methyl violet out of water. Clear colourless water is obtained after filtering. You can prove the dye must have been absorbed by the charcoal by pouring warm alcohol over the charcoal: the filtrate is now violet.

12.13 Subliming

There are a few substances which sublime on heating. The solid changes directly into a gas and, when cooled, the solid is re-formed.

Some substances which can sublime are solid carbon dioxide ('dry ice'), ammonium chloride and iodine (if heated rapidly). Thus to separate ammonium chloride from sodium chloride, the mixture could be heated in an evaporating basin with a cold funnel held above the basin, see Figure 12.7.

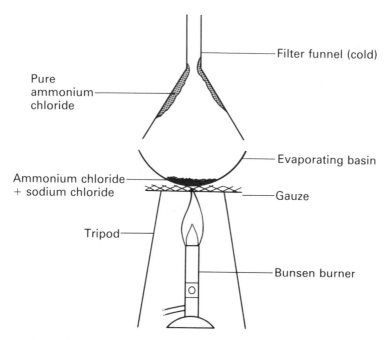

Fig. 12.7. An apparatus to separate a mixture by sublimation

12.14 Chemical separation

All the previous sections describe physical processes of separating mixtures. There are some mixtures which cannot be separated except by chemical processes. If you had a mixture of black copper(II) oxide and carbon you could separate them as follows: the copper(II) oxide will dissolve in warm, dilute sulphuric acid because of a chemical reaction.

copper(II) oxide + sulphuric acid → copper(II) sulphate solution

The copper sulphate solution is blue and it can easily be separated from carbon by filtration. Then copper(II) sulphate can be converted back into copper(II) oxide, see Section 10.3.

Dilute sulphuric acid can also be used to separate the alloy brass into copper and zinc. The zinc will dissolve in warm sulphuric acid giving zinc sulphate solution and hydrogen. Filtration then gives the copper. It is more difficult to get back the zinc – you must use electrolysis, see Chapter 14.

12.15 Some problems

These problems will be easier to solve when you are revising than on first reading this book.

Here is a list of mixtures. See if you can work out ways of separating them into their parts:

(a) sodium chloride (salt) and silicon dioxide (sand) as used for gritting roads;

(b) the green and yellow dyes that are in grass;

(c) iron and copper from a scrap car;

(d) calcium sulphate in water: a mixture known as permanently hard water – you probably drink it every day;

(e) potassium chloride and ammonium chloride;

(f) carbon dioxide and oxygen, two gases that are in the air;

(g) cork and broken glass;

(h) ammonia and nitrogen, two gases that are used to make fertilisers;

(i) screened methyl orange, a mixture which is an indicator (coloured substance) that you may use for titrations;

(j) sodium chloride (salt) and sucrose (sugar);

(k) copper and carbon;

(l) calcium carbonate (chalk) and sodium chloride (salt).

(Answers on page 267.)

13

Solutions

13.1 Saturated solutions

If you stir some salt into a beaker of water, at first the crystals disappear as they dissolve. The process of dissolving is called **dissolution**. Dissolution is like melting a solid (the solute) then mixing it with a liquid (the solvent) to give a solution. Many solid substances that you could not melt without decomposition can be broken down at ordinary temperatures to give solutions.

solute + solvent → solution

If you keep stirring salt into the beaker of water you find after a while that no more salt will dissolve. The solution is now **saturated** at that particular temperature. If you do try stirring in more salt the surplus just falls to the bottom. You know that a solution must be saturated if you see surplus crystals at the bottom. Movement of particles has not ceased, but as fast as some salt crystals are dissolving, others are forming. It is an example of **kinetic equilibrium**.

If you increase the temperature of the water, more salt dissolves before the solution is saturated.

The solubility of a solid in a solvent is the mass of the solid needed to saturate 1 kg of solvent, at a particular temperature.

A few scientists still consider the quantity of solvent to be 100 g, but now chemists often calculate concentrations in moles of solute per kg of solvent, see Chapters 35 and 37. If an aqueous solution is very dilute it is satisfactory to take 1 litre of solution as being close enough to 1 kg of water, when doing quick calculations.

13.2 Measuring solubility

A quick way of getting an approximate measurement of solubility is to weigh some saturated solution, boil off all the water and weigh the solute left. Sometimes boiling off all the water is difficult to do without losing some solution by spurting. Sometimes the solid left decomposes because it gets too hot. If you repeat the experiment with samples of solutions at different temperatures you can plot a graph of the results.

A second way of doing the experiment is to weigh out some solute, put it in a measured mass of solvent and warm them to see at what temperature the solute just dissolves. You can try to check your answer by seeing at what temperature the solute just starts to crystallise again. If you repeat the experiment with different masses of solute you can plot a graph of the results.

The most accurate method of measuring solubility is by doing a titration, see Section 23.3. You can measure the solubility of an acid by titration with an alkali or you can measure the solubility of an alkali by titration with an acid. Titrations can be done with other types of substances so the method can be used quite widely. You can do some experiments more accurately if you dilute the saturated solution carefully before doing the titration.

A solubility graph often curves upwards, like Figure 13.1. There

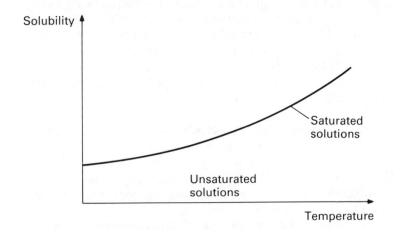

Fig. 13.1.   A typical solubility graph

are only a few solid substances whose solubility *decreases* as the temperature increases. However, for all gases the solubility decreases as the temperature increases. This is important in a river or even in an aquarium in summer – there is less oxygen in the water for the fish to breathe. If you take a fizzy drink from the fridge on a hot day the results can be rather like shaking a can and then opening it quickly – the carbon dioxide escapes rather fast!

13.3 Soluble or insoluble?

All acids are soluble in water; all the acids you will meet at this stage only act like acids when they are in aqueous solution. Very few bases are soluble in water, that is to say there are very few *alkalis*: sodium hydroxide, potassium hydroxide, calcium hydroxide and ammonia. Salts show a much greater variety of behaviour than acids and bases. Typical salts include the following:

(a) Hydrogencarbonates Sodium hydrogencarbonate is a solid which is not very soluble in water. Magnesium hydrogencarbonate and calcium hydrogencarbonate are only known as dilute solutions, see Section 3.1. No other hydrogencarbonates are known.

(b) Carbonates Only sodium carbonate, potassium carbonate and ammonium carbonate are soluble in water. All others are insoluble in water. Iron(III) carbonate and aluminium carbonate do not exist.

(c) Nitrates All nitrates are soluble in water.

(d) Sulphates Most sulphates are soluble in water. Barium sulphate is insoluble in water; if it is formed when testing a solution it shows the presence of a sulphate or of a barium compound. Calcium sulphate can be made by precipitation, but it is very slightly soluble: its solution is known as permanently hard water, see Section 3.1. Lead(II) sulphate can also be made by precipitation; its formation on the surface of a lead pipe in a house supplied with permanently hard water protects the people from lead poisoning.

(e) Chlorides Most chlorides are soluble in water. Silver chloride is insoluble in water. If it is formed when testing a solution it shows the presence of a chloride or of a silver compound. Lead(II) chloride can be made by precipitation but becomes much more soluble if the water is hot.

13.4 Alloys

Many metals are used in alloys instead of directly. An alloy is a solution or mixture of two or more metals. We make alloys to change the properties, sometimes physical, sometimes chemical, of the metals. Brass is harder than pure copper, duralumin is stronger than aluminium and stainless steel does not rust.

Magnesium alloyed with aluminium is used to make castings which have a high strength but low density, used for example in car wheels, for sheathing uranium in power stations and for aircraft parts, see Figure 13.2.

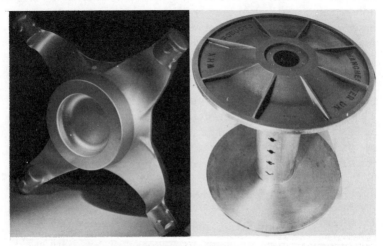

Fig. 13.2. Some articles made from magnesium alloys

Duralumin is an alloy of aluminium with copper and magnesium; nowadays some manganese is included and the alloy is called H14. Zinc is alloyed with aluminium to make zips and other castings.

Alloy steels are mixtures of iron with other elements. A typical stainless steel contains 73% iron, 18% chromium, 8% nickel and 1% carbon: it is used for sinks, cutlery, car exhausts and containers for many chemical processes. Tungsten steel is very hard and is used in armour plating and for high-speed tools. Manganese makes iron sufficiently hard for railway lines and rock-breaking machinery.

Vanadium, chromium and molybdenum are included in other alloy steels, often in complex mixtures.

Copper is mixed with zinc to make brass for water fittings and with tin to make bronze for architectural work. 1p and 2p coins are made of 97% copper, 2·5% zinc and 0·5% tin. Our so-called silver coins (5p, 10p and 50p) are an alloy of 75% copper and 25% nickel. 20p coins are an alloy of 84% copper and 16% nickel. The £1 coins contain 70% copper, 24·5% zinc and 5·5% nickel.

New uses for metals and alloys are found every year. Titanium is used now for artificial joints. Nickel alloys are used in jet planes for their heat resistance, see Figure 13.3.

Fig. 13.3. Nickel alloys are used in the exhausts for jet engines in planes

14

Electricity at Work

14.1 Electrolytes and non-electrolytes

For these experiments you need direct current (d.c.) electricity at 2–24 volts. You can get this from some ordinary dry cells (torch batteries, correctly known as voltaic cells, see Section 6.1) or from a 'power pack' – a transformer and a rectifier that can be run from the mains. You need two pieces of platinum or two carbon (graphite) rods. The apparatus can be set up as in Figure 14.1.

The **electrodes** are the pieces of metal or carbon (graphite) through which the electric current enters and leaves the electrolyte. The **anode** is the positive electrode. At this electrode, electrons

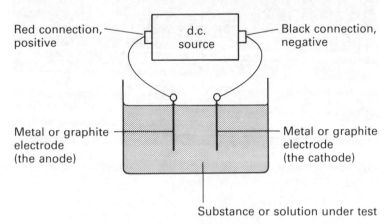

Red connection, positive

d.c. source

Black connection, negative

Metal or graphite electrode (the anode)

Metal or graphite electrode (the cathode)

Substance or solution under test

Fig. 14.1. An apparatus for investigating whether a solution conducts electricity

leave the electrolytic cell. Negative ions (anions) travel towards this electrode. Oxidation reactions occur at the anode. The **cathode** is the negative electrode. At this electrode, electrons enter the electrolytic cell. Positive ions (cations) travel towards the cathode. Reduction reactions occur at the cathode.

If you put some water into the beaker, whether it is distilled water or tap water, you will find that nothing happens. If you put sea water in the beaker then you will find that gases bubble off at the electrodes for as long as the electric current flows round the circuit. The main substance dissolved in sea water is sodium chloride, which is an ionic compound. The ions can move in the water and so the solution is a type of conductor called an electrolyte. Solid sodium chloride is a non-conductor because its ions are fixed in the crystal. If you melt sodium chloride then the ions can move and again you have a conductor called an electrolyte.

An **electrolyte** is a substance which, if melted or dissolved in water, conducts an electric current. Chemical reactions, called **electrolysis**, happen at the electrodes for as long as the current flows. A voltameter, or electrolytic cell, is the container in which electrolysis happens. A voltaic cell is the opposite type of cell to an electrolytic cell because in it a chemical reaction causes an electric current to flow in a circuit.

If you try the same experiment with sugar solution you will find that it is a non-conductor and is called a non-electrolyte. Sugar is a covalent compound and the crystals are made up of molecules. You can melt sugar by careful heating but the liquid is still a non-conductor, a non-electrolyte.

You can put an ammeter in the circuit to measure the current. You will find that you can divide electrolytes into three classes.

(*a*) *Strong electrolytes.* Most of these substances are acids, alkalis and salts, see Chapters 21–23. These substances are ionic in solution and so they are good conductors of electricity. The alkalis and salts are ionic also when solids.

(*b*) *Weak electrolytes*, for example some acids such as dilute ethanoic acid (vinegar) and some alkalis such as ammonia solution. These substances are a mixture of molecules and ions and so they are poor conductors of electricity. In these two examples, they are mostly molecules.

(*c*) *Non-electrolytes*. These substances are covalent solids, liquids or gases, for example sugar, alcohol and methane. They are non-conductors of electricity.

The importance of water as a solvent for many of these experiments can be seen by comparing

(*a*) hydrogen chloride gas dissolved in methylbenzene, which is a non-electrolyte, and

(*b*) hydrogen chloride gas dissolved in water (hydrochloric acid) which is a good electrolyte.

The covalent gas hydrogen chloride forms an ionic solution only in water.

An electric current in a metal wire or carbon (graphite) is a stream of **electrons**, tiny particles smaller than atoms, see Chapter 28. A solution or a melted substance is a conductor if there are **ions** in it and the ions can move. Ions are charged atoms or sets of atoms. These charged atoms are found in ionic substances, see Chapter 30.

14.2 The electrolysis of 'water'

A commonly used apparatus for electrolysis is Hofmann's voltameter, see Figure 14.2. August Hofmann (1818–92) was a German scientist who worked in the UK for many years.

Water is only a conductor of electricity if there is an acid, an alkali or a salt in it. So the 'water' in the voltameter is usually dilute sulphuric acid.

Platinum electrodes are the only good electrodes for this experiment. The power pack can be connected directly or an ammeter (or lamp) may be included with a variable resistor. The apparatus should be run for a few minutes to allow some of the gases produced to dissolve in the electrolyte.

The volume of hydrogen produced at the cathode is twice the volume of oxygen produced at the anode.

The electrolysis only proceeds for as long as the circuit is complete. This makes electrolysis different from heating substances with a Bunsen burner, where reactions often continue after the heat is turned off. Electricity and heating are both ways of supplying energy to substances.

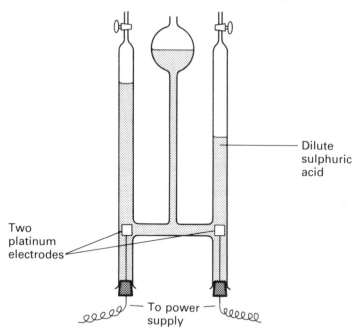

Fig. 14.2. A typical apparatus for the electrolysis of water: Hofmann's voltameter. Which electrode is the cathode?

There are several theories to explain electrolysis. Water is mostly covalent; there are very, very few hydrogen (H^+) and hydroxide (OH^-) ions in it. The sulphuric acid is ionic, being mostly hydrogen ions and sulphate ions (SO_4^{2-}), see Section 34.4. The 'selective discharge theory' says that when there is *dilute* sulphuric acid between inert (unreactive) electrodes, then the hydrogen and hydroxide ions are discharged, that is to say they react on the surface of the electrodes. The equations for these reactions are as follows.

At the cathode:

hydrogen ions   + electrons → hydrogen molecules
$2H^+(aq)$ $+ 2e^-$ $→ H_2(g)$

At the anode:

hydroxide ions → water molecules + oxygen molecules + electrons
$$4OH^-(aq) \rightarrow 2H_2O(l) \quad + O_2(g) \quad + 4e^-$$

For every four electrons going round the circuit, two hydrogen molecules and one oxygen molecule will be formed. This explains the different volumes of gases produced by the electrolysis. See also Chapters 33–34.

14.3 The electrolysis of liquid sodium chloride

If sodium chloride is heated to 800 °C it will melt. A mixture of 40% sodium chloride and 60% calcium chloride melts at 600 °C. This is electrolysed in a Downs' cell in industry to manufacture sodium (James Downs, USA). Electrolysis of the liquid (also called a molten or fused) mixture is the only way of making sodium on a large scale, see Figure 14.3. The chlorine produced at the same time

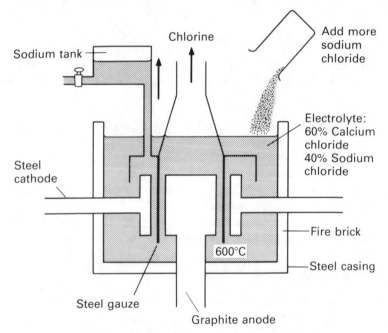

Fig. 14.3. The Downs' cell for making sodium

is not wasted, but there are cheaper ways of making it, see Section 14.4.

At the cathode:

sodium ions   + electrons $\rightarrow$ sodium atoms

$Na^+(l)$ $+ \ e^-$ $\rightarrow Na(l)$

You cannot use an aqueous solution of sodium chloride because sodium ions would not be discharged (hydrogen ions would be discharged at a steel cathode).

At the anode:

chloride ions $\rightarrow$ chlorine molecules   + electrons

$2Cl^-(l)$ $\rightarrow Cl_2(g)$ $+ \ 2e^-$

Sodium has a lower density than sodium chloride so it rises up into the tank and then is taken away and allowed to cool. The chlorine can be compressed and put into cylinders and taken to where it is needed.

14.4 The electrolysis of aqueous sodium chloride

If you electrolyse a *very* dilute solution of sodium chloride in water you will slowly get hydrogen at the cathode and oxygen at the anode. If you increase the concentration of the sodium chloride in the water it becomes obvious by the smell and colour that chlorine is also produced at the anode. The best material to use for the anode is carbon (graphite); iron (steel) or platinum or carbon (graphite) can be used for the cathode. If you test the solution near the cathode you will find that it is alkaline rather than neutral: sodium hydroxide has been formed.

This electrolysis is done in industry to make domestic bleach. The solution is stirred so that the chlorine formed at the anode can react with the sodium hydroxide formed at the cathode. The chemical name for bleach is sodium chlorate(I) or sodium hypochlorite. It is only known in solution. Bleach is used at home to remove stains from fabrics: it oxidises the coloured substances and makes them colourless. Bleach is now used to disinfect the water in swimming pools because it oxidises any germs. It is safer than using gaseous chlorine.

To make chlorine and sodium hydroxide separately on a large scale, many designs of electrolytic cell have been used. One early design used a mercury cathode: the solution of sodium in mercury (sodium amalgam) produced was mixed with water to give sodium hydroxide solution and hydrogen, then the mercury was returned to the cell. Another design had a sieve (a diaphragm of asbestos) between the anode and the cathode so that the sodium hydroxide solution and the chlorine were kept apart. The latest design is a membrane cell which works at 90 °C, see Figure 14.4.

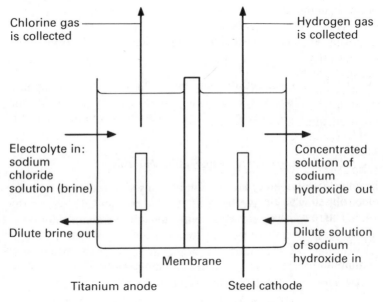

Fig. 14.4. A membrane cell

Chlorine is released at the titanium anode:

chloride ions $\rightarrow$ chlorine molecules + electrons

$2Cl^-(aq)$ $\rightarrow$ $Cl_2(g)$ + $2e^-$

The membrane only allows water and sodium ions to pass through. The flow of sodium ions is from the anode part of the cell to the cathode part.

Hydrogen ions from the water are discharged at the steel cathode:

hydrogen ions   + electrons $\rightarrow$ hydrogen molecules

$2H^+(aq)$ $+ 2e^-$ $\rightarrow H_2(g)$

From the cathode part, sodium hydroxide solution is drained off. The hydrogen is not wasted: see Section 17.9.

14.5 The electrolysis of aluminium oxide

The manufacture of aluminium is done in two stages. First impure aluminium oxide (bauxite) has to be purified to remove iron oxide because aluminium containing iron will corrode very quickly. This process uses a lot of sodium hydroxide and there is the problem of disposing of iron(III) oxide waste contaminated with sodium hydroxide. The aluminium oxide cannot be reduced with carbon because aluminium carbide would be formed. Liquid aluminium chloride is a non-conductor of electricity and so it cannot be used as an alternative electrolyte. If aqueous solutions of aluminium salts are used, aluminium ions are not discharged.

The second stage was discovered simultaneously in 1886, in the USA by Charles Hall (1863–1914) and in France by Paul Héroult (also 1863–1914). Aluminium oxide will dissolve in cryolite (sodium hexafluoroaluminate, Na_3AlF_6) at about 950 °C and can then be electrolysed. The electrodes are both carbon (graphite), see Figure 14.5. The reactions at the electrodes can be simplified as follows.

At the cathode:

aluminium ions + electrons $\rightarrow$ aluminium atoms

$Al^{3+}(l)$ $+ 3e^-$ $\rightarrow Al(l)$

At the anode:

oxygen ions $\rightarrow$ oxygen molecules + electrons

$2O^{2-}(l)$ $\rightarrow O_2(g)$ $+ 4e^-$

The aluminium is sucked out of the bottom of the cell and allowed to cool in moulds before being shaped for use. The oxygen attacks the red hot carbon anodes giving carbon monoxide and carbon dioxide. Fumes containing some fluorine compounds also come from the cell and so the gases must be filtered very carefully before letting them escape into the air. The cells are expensive to run because they use a lot of electricity (18 000 kW h for a tonne of aluminium) and because the carbon anodes have to be replaced frequently.

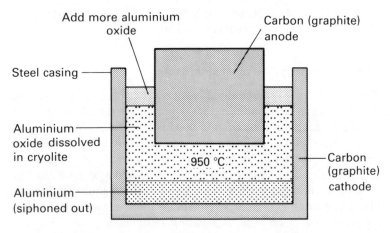

Fig. 14.5.   The electrolytic manufacture of aluminium

14.6 The electrolysis of aqueous copper(II) sulphate

This is a manufacturing process which can be done in the laboratory. The electrolyte is copper(II) sulphate solution and it is helpful to add a trace of dilute sulphuric acid. Both the electrodes are made of copper: the copper you want to purify is the anode, and the cathode is a thin piece of pure copper, see Figure 14.6.

At the cathode:

$$\text{copper ions} \quad + \text{electrons} \rightarrow \text{copper atoms}$$
$$Cu^{2+}(aq) \quad + 2e^- \quad\quad \rightarrow Cu(s)$$

At the anode:

$$\text{copper atoms} \rightarrow \text{copper ions} + \text{electrons}$$
$$Cu(s) \quad\quad \rightarrow Cu^{2+}(aq) \quad + 2e^-$$

The copper(II) sulphate solution remains unchanged because one copper ion forms at the anode for every copper ion discharged at the cathode. If the impurities in the copper anode are more

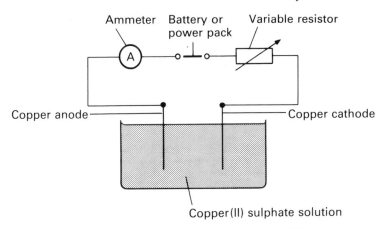

Fig. 14.6. The electrolysis of aqueous copper(II) sulphate

reactive metals (for example iron), they form ions which remain in solution. If the impurities in the copper anode are less reactive metals (for example silver and gold), they fall to the bottom of the cell as the anode sludge. Thus even sludge may be valuable.

Electrolysis can also be done to electroplate the cathode, using the same circuit. The object to be electroplated is used as the cathode. The solution must contain the metal to be used as the plating. To get good results in electrolysis experiments, it is important to have clean surfaces on the electrodes. You must use small currents so that things happen fairly slowly. A current of about 0·08 ampere for every square centimetre of the cathode may be the maximum that can be used without the new metal flaking off the cathode. In this way taps, cutlery, and parts for bicycles and cars are coated with chromium and nickel, or even silver or gold. The process saves using an expensive metal for the complete object. The electroplated metal may resist corrosion much better than the metal underneath. It may be harder and more resistant to wear. The electroplated metal may also be more beautiful or decorative than the metal underneath.

If the copper(II) sulphate solution is electrolysed using a platinum anode then the anode reaction is different. Oxygen is formed at the anode as in the electrolysis of water but copper is still deposited on the cathode whatever conductive material is used. The blue colour of the solution fades because the electrolyte becomes dilute sulphuric acid.

Can you work out what will happen if aqueous copper(II) chloride and molten lead(II) bromide are electrolysed (separately) between carbon (graphite) electrodes?

14.7 Faraday's laws of electrolysis

Quantities of electricity are measured in coulombs: you multiply the current in amperes by the time in seconds. Michael Faraday (England, 1791–1867) found two laws of electrolysis.

(*a*) The mass of an element made in electrolysis depends directly on the quantity of electricity used.
(*b*) The mass of an element made in electrolysis depends directly on its relative atomic mass divided by its valency.

The first law can be used to explain the volumes of gases made by electrolysis. The second law is useful in calculations, see Sections 35.7 and 36.3.

15

Making Metals

15.1 A survey

The more reactive a metal is, the harder it is to get it from its compounds. A summary of the metal industry is given in Figure 15.1. The metals have been put in the order known as the activity series, see Chapter 25.

(a) Metals at the top have to be obtained by the electrolysis of a molten compound. For example, sodium is made by the electrolysis of molten sodium chloride, see Section 14.3.

(b) Aluminium is made by the electrolysis of aluminium oxide dissolved in molten cryolite, see Section 14.5.

There must not be any water present in (a) or (b).

(c) Many metals are made by heating the metal oxide with carbon (coke). For example, iron in a blast furnace, see Section 15.2.

(d) Many metals are made or purified by the electrolysis of an aqueous solution of a compound. For example, copper is purified by the electrolysis of copper(II) sulphate solution, see Section 14.6.

(e) Many metals occur as their sulphides. These are difficult compounds to convert directly to the metals. The metal sulphide is heated in a stream of air. This gives the metal oxide and sulphur dioxide which is used to make sulphuric acid. Then the metal is obtained by method (c).

(f) The least reactive metals either occur native (that is to say, as elements) or can be made simply by heating a compound. For example, gold and silver occur naturally and mercury can be made by heating mercury(II) sulphide.

Metal or alloy	Source	Location of UK industry
Sodium	sodium chloride from underground in Cheshire	Cheshire, Cleveland, Lancashire
Aluminium	aluminium oxide imported from Jamaica, Brazil, Ghana & Greece. Aluminium metal imported from Norway	Anglesey, Cleveland, Fort William, Kinlochleven
Zinc	zinc sulphide imported from Peru, Australia, Ireland & Canada. Zinc metal imported from Netherlands, Finland & Canada	Avon
Iron	iron(III) oxide, iron(II) carbonate or iron(II) diiron(III) oxide mostly imported from Canada, Brazil & Australia	Cleveland, Clyde, Glamorgan, Lincolnshire
Steel	blast furnace iron and scrap iron	as iron plus West Midlands, Kent
Lead	lead(II) sulphide imported from Canada; lead metal imported from Australia & Canada	Avon
Copper	not much made in UK; new copper imported from Canada, Zambia and Chile	Lancashire, West Midlands and Yorkshire

Fig. 15.1.   The manufacture of metals

15.2 The manufacture of iron

Two common iron ores are haematite (Fe_2O_3) and magnetite (Fe_3O_4). These iron ores are usually imported. They are mixed with some coal and heated to 1200 °C. This is called sintering. The aim is

Extent of recycling	Energy requirements	Environmental problems	Annual tonnage used in the UK
not attempted	high	co-product chlorine	30 000
25%	high	fluorine compounds may escape	440 000
20%	moderate	co-product sulphur dioxide	240 000
80% used in making steel	moderate	smoke	7 000 000
50%	low	smoke	11 000 000
60%	moderate	lead fumes are poisonous; co-product sulphur dioxide	310 000
20%	moderate	co-product sulphur dioxide	540 000

to get lumps of a medium size and to remove any water and sulphur. If the lumps are too small they will get blown out of the blast furnace. If a lump is too big the iron ore at the centre will not be changed into iron. In the UK some iron(II) carbonate is mined. Sintering converts all ores into iron(II) diiron(III) oxide, Fe_3O_4, called iron oxide below.

Three substances are loaded on a large scale into the top of the blast furnace:

sintered iron ore (iron oxide)
carbon (as lumps of coke)
calcium carbonate (as lumps of limestone)

Huge quantities of air are heated and blown in near the base of the blast furnace through many small pipes. As the air moves up through the furnace the coke burns in two stages to give carbon monoxide:

$$\text{carbon} + \text{oxygen} \rightarrow \text{carbon dioxide}$$
$$C + O_2 \rightarrow CO_2$$
$$\text{carbon dioxide} + \text{carbon} \rightarrow \text{carbon monoxide}$$
$$CO_2 + C \rightarrow 2CO$$

The iron oxide is reduced to iron mainly by the carbon monoxide:

$$\text{iron oxide} + \text{carbon monoxide} \rightleftharpoons \text{iron} + \text{carbon dioxide}$$
$$Fe_3O_4 + 4CO \rightleftharpoons 3Fe + 4CO_2$$

The nitrogen (from the air) mixes with this carbon dioxide and also with surplus carbon monoxide. These gases come out of the top of the furnace and are cleaned, and the carbon monoxide in them is burnt to heat the air going in.

The sintering and these other reactions do not remove silicon dioxide (sand) from the iron ore. To do that the limestone is needed and, as in a limekiln, heating splits it up:

$$\text{calcium carbonate} \rightarrow \text{calcium oxide} + \text{carbon dioxide}$$
$$CaCO_3 \rightarrow CaO + CO_2$$

The calcium oxide (a basic oxide) combines with silicon dioxide (an acidic oxide) to give calcium silicate: this is called the **slag**.

$$\text{calcium oxide} + \text{silicon dioxide} \rightarrow \text{calcium silicate}$$
$$CaO + SiO_2 \rightarrow CaSiO_3$$

At high temperatures the slag is a liquid which floats on the molten iron at the bottom of the furnace, see Figure 15.2. First the slag is drained from the furnace and then the iron. The slag can be

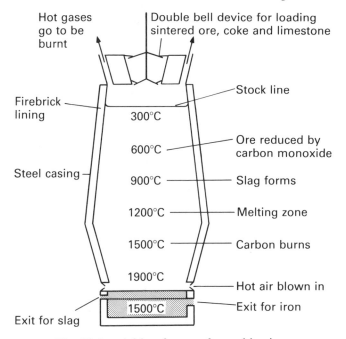

Fig. 15.2. A blast furnace for making iron

used for making roads and cement or even as a fertiliser because it may contain phosphorus. The iron, sometimes called pig iron, is not pure. It may contain up to 5% carbon (which makes it brittle) and smaller percentages of sulphur, phosphorus and silicon. It is used to make pipes, manhole covers and the frames of stoves and machinery.

15.3 The manufacture of steel

Most iron from the blast furnace is made into steel. A steel is iron mixed with less than 1·5% carbon. Although steel is softer than iron it is not so brittle. The furnace is called a Basic Oxygen Converter. Oxygen is blown into the molten iron to convert the non-metals (sulphur, phosphorus and carbon) into their oxides. The furnace is lined with bricks made of calcium oxide and magnesium oxide (made from dolomite, $MgCO_3 \cdot CaCO_3$). These oxides are basic so they remove the acidic oxides as a slag. The converter is tipped clockwise to let out the slag and then the other way to pour out the steel.

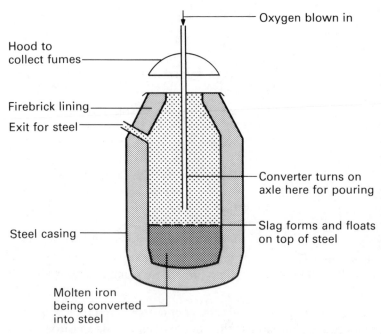

Fig. 15.3.   A furnace for the manufacture of steel

15.4 The properties of metals

The general physical properties of metals were listed in Figure 11.2. In the periodic table of the elements (Chapter 29) the metals are put in the low-numbered groups to the left and in the centre. The atomic number of an element also tells you the total number of electrons in an atom. The number of electrons in the outer shell, written last, often tells you the valency of an element. Hence you can work out the formulae of its compounds, see Chapters 28 and 33. Typical metals have high densities and melting points when compared with typical non-metals.

	Group	Atomic number	Electronic structure	Relative atomic mass	Density (g/ml)	Melting point/°C
Lithium	1	3	2,1	7	0·53	180
Sodium	1	11	2,8,1	23	0·97	98
Potassium	1	19	2,8,8,1	39	0·86	63
Magnesium	2	12	2,8,2	24	1·7	650
Calcium	2	20	2,8,8,2	40	1·6	850
Iron	–	26	2,8,14,2	56	7·9	1 535
Copper	–	29	2,8,18,1	64	9·0	1 080
Zinc	–	30	2,8,18,2	65	7·1	419
Aluminium	3	13	2,8,3	27	2·7	660
Lead	4	82	2,8,18,32, 18,4	207	11·3	327

Fig. 15.4.   The physical properties of metals

Notice in Figure 15.4 that the metals in groups 1 and 2 have low melting points and densities. Outside the laboratory they are not so well known as metals. The chemical properties of metals are given in Chapter 25, where they are used to sort the metals into an order of activity (reactivity). The crystal structures of metals are discussed in Section 32.3.

15.5 The uses of metals

Sodium is used in the manufacture of sodium compounds that are difficult to make in any other way, such as sodium cyanide for gold and silver manufacture, and sodium peroxide (Na_2O_2) for bleaching. Sodium lamps light most of our streets by night.

Iron. Some iron is used directly from the blast furnace in castings for cars, machinery, pipes and manhole covers. Iron is the catalyst in the manufacture of ammonia, see Section 18.3.

Steel is used on a large scale for buildings (direct or for reinforcing concrete), ships, cars, trains, tools and machinery, and on a small scale in nuts, bolts, nails and screws. A lot of food is sold in 'tin' cans: the layer of tin covering the steel is very thin indeed.

Copper is used mainly as wire for conducting electricity and in alloys. Some copper is used for car radiators and central heating or water pipes.

Zinc is mainly used in alloys and to protect iron against rusting, see Section 7.9.

Aluminium is used in alloys for the construction of planes, boats, trains, cars and lorries. Aluminium wires, with a steel core for strength, carry electricity around the country on pylon lines. Many window frames, pots, pans and kettles are made of aluminium. Aluminium foil is used in packaging food.

Lead is used to cover electricity cables, and for roofing and damp-proof courses in buildings. Lead and lead(IV) oxide are used in car batteries and, at the moment, a lead compound is added to most petrol to increase its efficiency in an engine. Lead bricks are used to shield people when doing radioactivity experiments and in hospitals to shield radiographers from the X-rays they use to examine patients.

16

Compounds of Metals

16.1 Sodium chloride

Sodium chloride is common salt, the best example of a salt. It occurs in sea water (about 27 g/l) and as rock salt in dried up sea beds, for example underground in Cheshire. In southern France and in Australia sea water is trapped and left to evaporate. The salt crystallises out as the water evaporates in the heat from the sun.

The rock salt in Cheshire can be mined in the same way as underground coal, but most is obtained by 'solution mining'. Water is pumped down to the salt 'beds', it dissolves the salt and the solution is pumped up. Very often the solution is used directly in industry but some is evaporated to give us crystals of salt. Rock salt can be purified by dissolving the salt in water, filtering off the clay that was with it and evaporating the solution to give crystals.

Salt is an essential part of our diet. We may lose too much of it through sweating in hot weather, and have to take extra. Normally we eat enough in vegetables and other foods. If we eat too much salt our blood pressure may rise too high. Salt is used as a preservative for bacon, fish and vegetables.

Industry uses salt to make sodium (see Section 14.3) and sodium hydroxide, chlorine and domestic bleach, see Section 14.4. For the effect of salt on the properties of water see Section 9.1. Salt in water increases the rate of rusting, see Section 7.9. For the crystal structure of salt see Section 30.2.

16.2 Sodium hydroxide

The manufacture of sodium hydroxide was described in Section 14.4. You may use it usually as a colourless solution but it can be crystallised as a white solid. It is also called caustic (burning) soda because it is very corrosive. It is a cheap, strong alkali, see Chapter 22. It is very useful in analysis for finding the cation in an unknown salt, see Figure 22.1. Industry uses a lot of sodium hydroxide for making viscose rayon, paper, domestic bleach, soap and for purifying bauxite when making aluminium, see Section 14.5.

16.3 Sodium carbonate

Sodium carbonate is manufactured on a large scale from sodium chloride and calcium carbonate by the Solvay process. At home you may use washing soda, which is sodium carbonate-10-water, to soften hard water, see Section 3.2.

Most sodium carbonate is used to manufacture glass by heating it with calcium carbonate, silicon dioxide (sand) and some recycled broken glass to about 1500 °C and then letting it cool slowly. Glass does not have a definite melting point. If potassium carbonate is used instead of sodium carbonate the glass is harder (more resistant to heat). If lead(II) oxide is included, then a glass suitable for 'cut glass' bowls and glasses is obtained.

Fig. 16.1 A cut glass bowl

Sodium hydrogencarbonate is used in baking powder because it will give carbon dioxide when it is heated alone or with acids – the gas makes your cakes rise. Sodium hydrogencarbonate is found in several indigestion medicines, see Section 22.4.

16.4 Calcium compounds

Calcium carbonate is found in nature as chalk, limestone and marble: chalk is the softest and marble the hardest. There are many quarries for calcium carbonate, unfortunately often in National Parks or Areas of Outstanding Natural Beauty, see Figure 4.1. The direct use of calcium carbonate in agriculture was mentioned in Section 7.5. When calcium carbonate dissolves in acidic rainwater it gives temporarily hard water, see Section 3.1. Calcium carbonate is used in making iron, see Section 15.2, sodium carbonate and glass, and for roads and buildings. To make cement, calcium carbonate is heated with clay to 1500 °C and some calcium sulphate is added to control the rate of setting, see Figure 16.2.

Fig. 16.2. Cement kilns at Northfleet, Kent

When calcium carbonate is heated in a limekiln calcium oxide is formed. The nitrogen of the air pushes out the carbon dioxide produced:

| calcium carbonate | $\rightarrow$ | calcium oxide | + | carbon dioxide |
| $CaCO_3$ | $\rightarrow$ | CaO | + | CO_2 |

The reaction occurs quickly at 1150 °C. Calcium oxide is a typical basic oxide. It is used with magnesium oxide to make bricks to line furnaces. It is sometimes called quicklime because its reaction with water is vigorous, and any lumps will expand and then crumble. The product is calcium hydroxide, also called slaked lime.

Calcium hydroxide is used in gardening (see Section 7.5), to neutralise acidic waste liquids, to soften water (see Section 3.2), in processing sewage, in making leather and in sugar refining. In the laboratory, calcium hydroxide solution (limewater) is the reagent used to prove the presence of carbon dioxide, see Figure 21.2. In this test calcium carbonate is reformed.

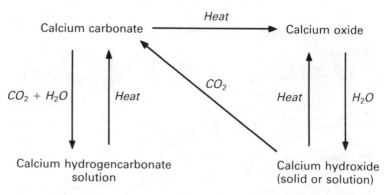

Fig. 16.3.   Some reactions of calcium compounds

17

Making Non-metals

17.1 A survey

The more reactive a non-metal is, the harder it is to get it from its compounds. The non-metals can be put in an activity order by comparing the reactivity of each one with the same metal. The order can be checked by an electrical experiment in which voltages are measured, see Sections 6.1 and 25.2.

fluorine   chlorine   oxygen   bromine   iodine
(most reactive)   (least reactive)

(a) The most reactive non-metal, fluorine, has to be made by electrolysis of a molten compound.

(b) The very reactive non-metals can be made by electrolysis of aqueous solutions of their compounds. For example, chlorine is made by the electrolysis of aqueous sodium chloride, see Section 14.4.

(c) Many non-metals are made by oxidation of their compounds. For example, chlorine can be made by oxidation of hydrochloric acid and bromine is manufactured by passing chlorine into acidified sea water, see Section 17.3.

(d) The least reactive non-metals occur naturally. For example, carbon occurs as diamond and graphite, and sulphur occurs underground in several parts of the world. Oxygen is fairly reactive but has not all disappeared into compounds because its proportion in the air is continually renewed, see Section 7.1.

(e) Non-metals are made by a wider variety of methods than metals. For example, in industry oxygen is made from the air (see Section 1.2), and in the laboratory it is made by the catalytic decomposition of hydrogen peroxide.

| | | | | *Group* | | |
Period	III	IV	V	VI	VII	0
1						helium
2	boron	carbon	nitrogen	oxygen	fluorine	neon
3		silicon	phosphorus	sulphur	chlorine	argon
4			arsenic	selenium	bromine	krypton
5				tellurium	iodine	xenon
6					astatine	radon

Fig. 17.1.   The non-metals of the periodic table

The noble gases (group 0) are unreactive. The most reactive of the non-metals is fluorine, which is near the top right of the periodic table, and the least reactive are those such as silicon which are closest to the boundary with metals, see Figure 17.1.

17.2 Chlorine

Chlorine can be made in the laboratory by several methods in which chloride ions are oxidised by loss of electrons, see Section 24.6.

(*a*) Heat concentrated hydrochloric acid with manganese(IV) oxide, see Figure 17.2.
(*b*) Heat a mixture of sodium chloride crystals, manganese(IV) oxide and concentrated sulphuric acid.
(*c*) Pour concentrated hydrochloric acid onto potassium manganate(VII) crystals. Be careful you have the correct reagents.
(*d*) Electrolysis of hydrochloric acid or a solution of a chloride. The anode must be made of carbon (graphite), see Section 14.4.

Chlorine should be made in the fume cupboard because it is a poisonous gas. You can collect it by downward delivery because it is more dense than air. It has a yellow-green colour and a very strong smell. It can be collected over water, but it is fairly soluble and so you will lose some.

Chlorine bleaches damp litmus paper: if you use the blue paper you will see it go red first, then white. Only wet chlorine will bleach.

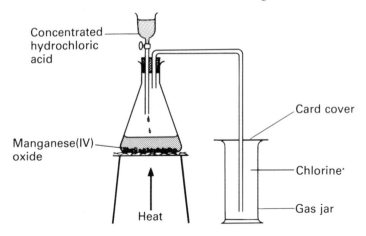

Fig. 17.2.   The laboratory preparation of chlorine

It forms hydrochloric acid and chloric(I) acid, also called hypo-chlorous acid, HClO. It is the chloric(I) acid which causes bleaching, by oxidation. Domestic bleach is sodium chlorate(I), also called sodium hypochlorite, NaClO. This is now used to disinfect swimming pool water.

The other important uses of chlorine are for making PVC (a plastic, see Section 20.1), for making solvents for dry cleaning, metal-degreasing and liquid paper, for bleaching wood pulp, for sterilising drinking water and for making many compounds for refrigerator liquids, pesticides, weedkillers, antiseptics and anaesthetics.

Chlorine is a vigorous oxidising agent, see Chapter 24. It will change hot iron to iron(III) chloride and hot aluminium to aluminium chloride. Both these compounds are used as catalysts and iron(III) chloride is used also in making printed circuits. Chlorine will convert iron(II) ions in solution into iron(III) ions, so you will see a colour change from pale green to pale yellow.

17.3 The halogens

The halogens (the 'salt formers') are the elements in group VII of the periodic table,

fluorine	chlorine	bromine	iodine	astatine
F	Cl	Br	I	At

Fluorine is too dangerous as an element for you to use in many experiments. If chlorine is passed into a solution of a bromide then bromine is formed: this is the way bromine is manufactured from sea and spring water. If chlorine or bromine is passed into a solution of an iodide then iodine is formed. These *displacement reactions* also show that each halogen is a better oxidising agent than those below it in the periodic table. The more reactive halogen atom gains an electron to become a halide ion. The smaller the atom the more readily this reaction occurs, so chlorine is a better oxidising agent than bromine and bromine is a better oxidising agent than iodine.

	Chlorine	*Bromine*	*Iodine*
Atomic number	17	35	53
Melting point/ °C	−101	−7	113
Boiling point/ °C	−34	59	184
State at room temperature	gas	liquid	solid
Relative atomic mass and density (if a gas) (compared to hydrogen)	35·5	80	127
Colour	pale yellow-green	red-brown	black if solid, purple if gas

Fig. 17.3.   Properties of three of the halogens

The halogens are a good example of a group or family of elements in the periodic table. They all have 7 electrons in the outer shell of the atom and have a valency of one. With metals they form ionic compounds and with non-metals they form covalent compounds. The halogens exist as diatomic molecules so we write their formulae as F_2, Cl_2, Br_2, I_2 and At_2. As the atomic number increases, many properties show a steady change, see Figure 17.3.

17.4 Oxygen

Oxygen is the most common element in the rocks of the earth's surface: it is found in many compounds. It is the second most abundant element in the air. Oxygen is also the most abundant element in sea water, where it occurs in several compounds as well as in water itself.

Oxygen is manufactured from air, see Section 1.2. In the laboratory, oxygen is usually made by the catalytic decomposition of hydrogen peroxide. (A catalyst is a substance that increases the rate of some reactions.) Oxygen has almost the same density as air so the best way of collecting it is over water, as in Figure 17.4. Some oxygen is lost because the gas is slightly soluble.

$$\text{hydrogen peroxide} \rightarrow \text{water} + \text{oxygen}$$
$$2H_2O_2(aq) \rightarrow 2H_2O(l) + O_2(g)$$

Oxygen can also be made by the electrolysis of solutions, for example dilute sulphuric acid, see Section 14.2. Oxygen escapes when many compounds are heated, for example potassium manganate(VII), lead(IV) oxide, sodium nitrate and silver oxide.

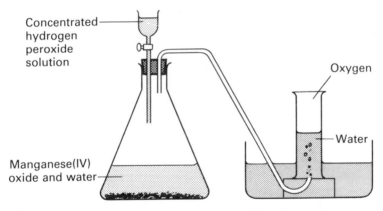

Concentrated hydrogen peroxide solution

Oxygen

Water

Manganese(IV) oxide and water

Fig. 17.4. The laboratory preparation of oxygen

The test for oxygen is that it will relight a glowing splint. The wood will burn more easily in pure oxygen than in air, which is only one-fifth oxygen. Oxygen has no smell and no colour. It is neutral to litmus. Oxygen has six electrons in the outer shell of the atom and its valency is two, see Sections 28.4 and 33.3.

Oxygen is vital for the combustion of fuels, for respiration, for the rusting of iron and for the rotting of many things that we throw away.

It is used to support life in many extreme situations: in space ships, in hospitals, especially if you have an anaesthetic. For diving, oxygen is diluted with helium which is almost insoluble in blood: this is an improvement over using nitrogen and the danger of 'bends' is reduced. The greatest amount of oxygen used is in the steel industry, see Section 15.3. Other large users are industries which cut and weld metals, often by using oxygen–acetylene (ethyne) flames. The most spectacular use of oxygen is its use with hydrogen to power space rockets.

17.5 Oxides

Most elements except the noble gases will burn when they are heated in oxygen. Metals such as sodium and magnesium burn vigorously. They give basic oxides which are ionic and react with water to give alkaline solutions: sodium hydroxide is very soluble in water but magnesium hydroxide is only slightly soluble. Like most metals, iron filings will burn in air – you see sparks – and a basic oxide, Fe_3O_4, is formed which is insoluble in water.

A few metals, their oxides and their hydroxides, are amphoteric, see Section 22.3.

Non-metals such as carbon and sulphur will burn in oxygen to give dioxides if they are heated. These oxides are covalent and with water give acids. If the supply of air is limited, carbon gives carbon monoxide which is poisonous. A few non-metal oxides are neutral, for example, water, carbon monoxide, nitrogen monoxide (NO) and dinitrogen oxide (N_2O).

17.6 Sulphur

Sulphur occurs underground as an element. It is mined in the USA and Poland by melting it with very hot water (at 170 °C under ten times normal pressure) and then blowing the mixture back to the surface with hot compressed air. This is called the Frasch process. When the mixture gets to the surface it quickly separates into three parts again. Sulphur is produced also when crude oil (petroleum) is refined. Natural gas from some wells is 'sour' because it contains hydrogen sulphide which must be removed before the gas can be used. The hydrogen sulphide is then converted to sulphur.

Sulphur is a yellow solid with a low melting point (119 °C) and boiling point (445 °C). It is brittle and is a non-conductor of electricity. Sulphur shows allotropy, see Section 32.4 and Figure 17.5.

Property	Rhombic	Monoclinic
Crystal shape	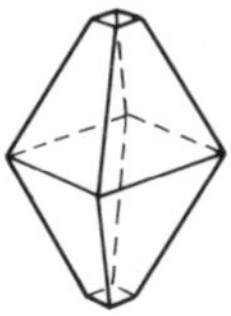 (octahedral)	 (simplified)
Stability	up to 96 °C	96–119 °C
Density (g/ml)	2·07	1·96
Molecules	S_8 rings packed tightly	S_8 rings packed loosely
Appearance	amber-yellow, transparent	pastel yellow, translucent

Fig. 17.5. The allotropy of sulphur

Many metals will combine with sulphur if they are heated together.

The most important use of sulphur is in the manufacture of sulphuric acid, see Section 18.2. Its other uses include making sulphur dioxide, vulcanising rubber (making the natural latex into a useful substance) and in making many medicines and pesticides.

Sulphur dioxide is a poisonous gas with a strong smell. It is the best known pollutant of the air we breathe, see Section 1.3. It is a bleach but it is not as useful as chlorine because it bleaches by reduction and atmospheric oxidation may reverse this. It is used as a food preservative, for example in jam, and for sterilising things such as home brewing equipment (Campden tablets produce sulphur dioxide in solution).

17.7 Nitrogen

Nitrogen is the unreactive part of the air. For its manufacture see Section 1.2. In the laboratory it can be made by trying to remove the other gases from air, which leaves some argon in it, or by heating certain substances, for example ammonium dichromate(VI), which is expensive.

Nitrogen is a colourless gas with no smell. It is only very slightly soluble in water and the solution is neutral. It puts out a burning splint and does not affect calcium hydroxide solution. The only other gases in air which have nearly the same properties are argon and the other noble gases.

Nitrogen is the key element in animal and plant proteins. Only a few plants (leguminous ones) can absorb the nitrogen directly from the air, see Section 7.4. The farmer has to use nitrogen fertilisers to get high yields of crops. The industrialist makes many nitrogen compounds to help the farmer, see Section 7.5.

The main use of nitrogen is to make ammonia and then nitric acid, see Sections 18.3 and 18.4. Nitrogen is also used as the inert (unreactive) gas in tungsten filament electric light bulbs, for flushing out oil tanks and pipelines and for the storage of apples. Liquid nitrogen is very cold (-196 °C) and is used as a refrigerating agent for freeze-drying food and for the storage of blood and the corneas of eyes.

17.8 Carbon

Carbon occurs naturally as diamond and graphite: these crystalline forms are **allotropes**, see Section 32.4 and Figure 17.6. Most of the diamonds and graphite used in industry are now manufactured. Diamonds used as gemstones are always natural crystals. These two forms of carbon both consist of giant molecules, containing many atoms linked by covalent bonds. Their structures can be used to explain their properties.

Carbon occurs in many compounds and mixtures found in nature. It is present in the carbonates of sodium, calcium and zinc, in sugars, starches, plants, wood, oil, natural gas, coal and all flesh. For the carbon cycle see Figure 7.3.

Carbon will burn if it is heated. In plenty of air it gives carbon

Property	Diamond	Graphite
Shape of crystals	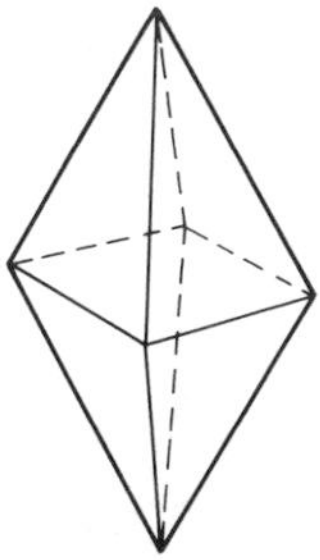 (octahedral)	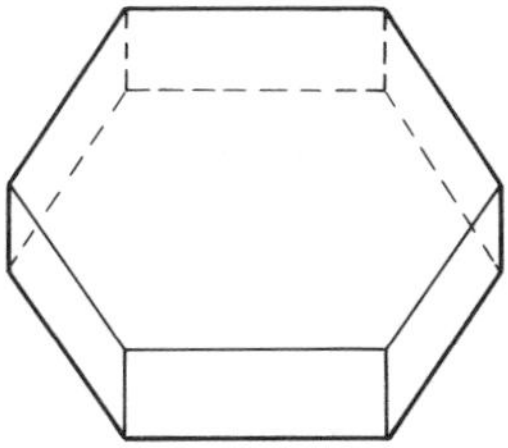 (planar hexagonal)
Arrangement of atoms	 tetrahedral – continuously to edge of crystal	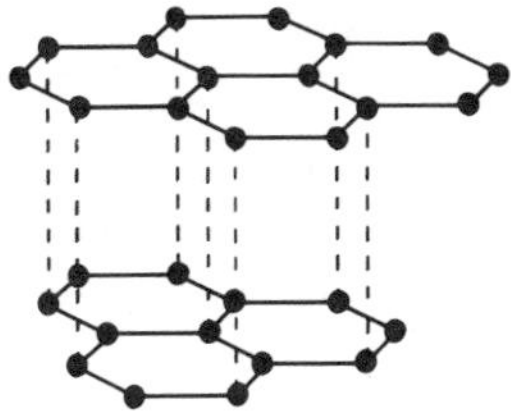 in widely spaced sheets of hexagons (staggered)
Appearance	transparent, colourless, shiny	opaque, black, shiny
Hardness	the hardest naturally-occurring substance, scratches or cuts all other substances	flakes easily so feels softer, more greasy, and marks paper (it is the 'lead' in pencils)
Electrical conductivity	none	fairly good, used in electrodes
Density (g/ml)	3·51	2·25

Fig. 17.6.   The physical properties of the allotropes of carbon

dioxide, in a limited supply of air it gives carbon monoxide, the same as most fuels. Carbon is used as the reducing agent in the blast furnace for producing iron and in making many other metals, see Section 15.3.

17.9 Hydrogen

Hydrogen is an element which it is difficult to classify so it is often put on its own at the top of the periodic table, see Figure 29.1. Hydrogen ions are positive and go to the cathode in electrolysis, the same as metallic ions. The hydrogen ion on its own is just the nucleus of the atom. Like metallic ions, hydrogen ions in solutions have water molecules attached to them and so they are sometimes written as H_3O^+ rather than H^+, but it is better to be less precise and to write $H^+(aq)$. Hydrogen is like the non-metallic halogens because it forms a diatomic molecule, H_2, it is a gas and it can form a negative ion, H^- (but this is rare).

Hydrogen is formed in the electrolysis of water (see Section 14.2), also in many other reactions. Many metals will react with water or steam to give hydrogen – the results can be used to put metals in the order known as the activity series, see Chapter 25. The metals of moderate reactivity react with dilute hydrochloric or dilute sulphuric acid to give hydrogen. A typical apparatus for a laboratory experiment is shown in Figure 17.7.

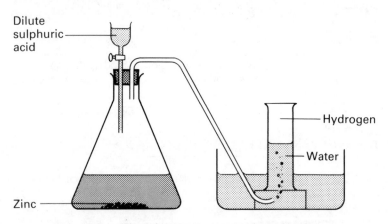

Fig. 17.7.   The laboratory preparation of hydrogen

In industry hydrogen is made by the steam reforming of natural gas. The gases at high pressure are sent over a nickel–chromium catalyst at 750 °C:

methane + steam $\rightleftharpoons$ carbon monoxide + hydrogen

CH_4 + H_2O $\rightleftharpoons$ CO + $3H_2$

Further stages of the process convert the carbon monoxide to carbon dioxide (a useful by-product) and purify the hydrogen. Some hydrogen is produced by the electrolysis of brine, see Section 14.4.

Hydrogen is the gas with the lowest density. Other gases are often compared to it and the result is given as the relative density or vapour density. For example, the relative density of carbon dioxide is 22 and of air, as an average, 14.4.

Hydrogen was used in airships but its dangerous flammability soon led to helium being preferred. Hydrogen in a laboratory experiment could be collected in a gas jar by upward delivery but you would not know when the gas jar was full. It is safer to collect it over water, in which it is not very soluble.

Hydrogen and air (or oxygen) can be a dangerously explosive mixture. The test for hydrogen is only safe when done on a small scale in an open test tube, see Figure 21.1. A small explosion, sometimes described as a high-pitched or squeaky 'pop', is given when a lighted splint is held at the mouth of the tube. The hydrogen burns to give water in a very exothermic reaction, see Section 26.1. If pure hydrogen comes out of a jet it can be burnt safely in air. Could hydrogen be a fuel for the future, or is it only useful in rockets? There are no pollution problems.

hydrogen + oxygen $\rightarrow$ water

$2H_2(g)$ + $O_2(g)$ $\rightarrow$ $2H_2O(l)$; ΔH = -572 kJ/mol

Hydrogen is a good reducing agent but because of the dangers and expense it is not used as much as carbon or methane.

Hydrogen is used on a large scale to make ammonia, methanol and nylon, to help in the refining of oil and as a liquid to cool low temperature memories for computers (-253 °C). Hydrogen is used to harden many vegetable oils (liquids) so that they are fats (solids at room temperature). At five times normal pressure and at 180 °C in the presence of a nickel catalyst, the hydrogen reacts with the oil to give fats suitable for margarine or cooking.

17.10 The noble gases

The noble gases are the members of group 0 of the periodic table, see Figure 17.1. A few people call them group 8, but historically that means iron, cobalt and nickel with the elements beneath them in the table. A new version of the periodic table suggests calling them group 18 (look at Figure 29.1 to see why). At one time they were called the rare gases, but we now know that argon (0·9%) is much more abundant in the air than carbon dioxide and often more abundant than water vapour. Another title they have had is the inert gases, but after many years of experiments it has been found that xenon, krypton and radon *do* react to form quite a few compounds. Helium is found sometimes with natural gas. Most of the noble gases can be obtained by the careful distillation of liquid air. Radon, the most dense noble gas, is radioactive. It escapes from traces of uranium in granite and other rocks and in some areas, such as Cornwall and north east Scotland, good ventilation of buildings is important to prevent it becoming a hazard to the inhabitants.

The electronic structures of the first three members are important to us:

helium	He	2
neon	Ne	2,8
argon	Ar	2,8,8

In nearly all simple ionic and covalent compounds, the atoms of elements get the electronic structures of the nearest noble gases, see Chapters 30 and 31. All the noble gases except helium have 8 electrons in the outer shell of the atom and so the theory of valency is sometimes called the octet theory. The noble gases are almost completely unreactive and the reason for this must be that their electronic structures are stable compared to the structures of the nearby elements in the periodic table.

The noble gases are used in glass tubes with electrodes to give coloured lights; for example neon gives a red glow. This is the colour of many street lights while the sodium in them is being warmed. Argon and helium are used to push air out of the way when some metals are being cut or welded: this prevents oxygen in the air reacting with the hot metal. Argon is better than nitrogen in electric light bulbs because the tungsten filament will last longer. Helium is the best gas to mix with oxygen for divers to breathe, see Section 17.4.

18

Compounds of Non-metals

18.1 Hydrogen chloride and hydrochloric acid

Hydrogen chloride is manufactured by burning hydrogen in chlorine. Mixtures of the two gases will explode if ignited. In the laboratory, hydrogen chloride can be made by carefully pouring concentrated sulphuric acid onto sodium chloride crystals.

$$H_2SO_4(l) + NaCl(s) \rightarrow NaHSO_4(s) + HCl(g)$$

The residue left in the flask is sodium hydrogensulphate. Hydrogen chloride is a covalent gas which has a strong smell and is poisonous. It is more dense than air so it can be collected by downward delivery, see Figure 18.1. It is very soluble in water and care is

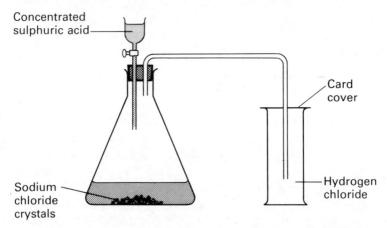

Fig. 18.1. The laboratory preparation of hydrogen chloride

needed when making it into a solution. The best method is the inverted funnel method, see Figure 21.3. The funnel must only just dip into the water to give a wide area for the gas to dissolve in the water. The solution of the gas in water contains ions and is called hydrochloric acid.

There is a fun way of making hydrogen chloride into hydrochloric acid, called the fountain experiment. Fill a flask with hydrogen chloride made as above. The hydrogen chloride is at normal atmospheric pressure as it fills the flask by downward delivery. Put a glass tube in a stopper into the neck of the flask. The glass tube should be full of water at the start and have a rubber tube and clip at one end, see Figure 18.2. Put a few drops of blue litmus solution (with ammonia if necessary) into a bowl of water. Hold the flask neck upwards and for one second release the clip so that a drop of water falls into the flask. This drop of water dissolves some hydrogen chloride so the pressure inside the flask is now less than normal. Turn the flask so that it is as shown in the figure and open the clip under water. A stream of water flows into the flask up the tube and gives a fountain. The solution becomes acidic so the litmus turns red.

Hydrochloric acid is a typical strong acid, see Chapter 21. The concentrated acid in the laboratory is a saturated solution of hydrogen chloride in water (about 12 mol/l). Both the gas and the acid oxidise metals, forming salts and hydrogen. The concentrated

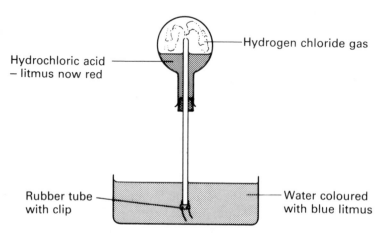

Fig. 18.2. The fountain experiment

acid is a reducing agent for manganese(IV) oxide, see Section 17.2. The test for a chloride is described in Section 23.5(c).

Hydrochloric acid is used to make glucose from starch, glue from bones and to clean metal surfaces before electroplating. The gas is used to make PVC, see Section 20.1.

18.2 Sulphuric acid

Sulphuric acid is manufactured on a large scale. Sulphur is melted and sprayed into a furnace where it burns in plenty of air, giving sulphur dioxide.

$$S(l) + O_2(g) \rightarrow SO_2(g)$$

In the contact process the sulphur dioxide and excess air are passed over a catalyst, vanadium(V) oxide, V_2O_5, at about 420 °C. This gives a high yield of sulphur trioxide.

$$2SO_2(g) + O_2(g) \rightarrow 2SO_3(g)$$

The sulphur trioxide cannot be dissolved directly in water because it forms a mist which is hard to condense – atmospheric pollution on a grand scale. So it is dissolved in concentrated sulphuric acid which is poured into water to keep the concentration at about 98% H_2SO_4.

$$H_2O(l) + SO_3(g) \rightarrow H_2SO_4(aq)$$

The process is easy to do, so sulphuric acid factories are generally close to the industrial users of the acid. This saves transport costs and is safer.

To make concentrated sulphuric acid into dilute sulphuric acid you must always pour the concentrated acid into water, stirring carefully. The danger if you do this the wrong way round is that some acid may spit out. The concentrated acid consists mostly of covalent molecules and the dilute acid of ions. The concentrated acid is a very dangerous liquid because of its vigorous reaction with water and with substances that contain water. It will take water out of copper(II) sulphate-5-water crystals, turning them from blue to white. It will take water out of sugar, turning it into a huge lump of charcoal like a black sponge. The concentrated acid is therefore a dehydrating agent. Sometimes it is used to dry gases, except for ammonia with which it forms ammonium sulphate.

Fig. 18.3. A factory for making sulphuric acid in Eire

When the concentrated acid reacts with sodium chloride crystals (see Section 18.1) it is behaving as a non-volatile substance: it has a very much higher boiling point (338 °C) than hydrogen chloride (−85 °C).

Dilute sulphuric acid is a typical strong acid, see Chapter 21. When the cold, dilute acid reacts with magnesium, zinc and iron or when the hot, concentrated acid reacts with copper, then the acid is behaving as an oxidising agent. The test for a sulphate is described in Section 23.5(b).

About a third of the sulphuric acid made is used to manufacture calcium dihydrogenphosphate (superphosphate) and ammonium sulphate, which are both fertilisers. Large quantities are used in the manufacture of titanium(IV) oxide (for paints and for titanium metal), soapless detergents, man-made fibres and other sulphates. Iron may be dipped into dilute sulphuric acid to clean the surface before it is electroplated. The acid in a car battery is moderately concentrated sulphuric acid.

18.3 Ammonia

The synthesis of ammonia was discovered by Fritz Haber (1868–1934, Germany). Hydrogen is made as described in Section 17.9. A small modification to the process brings in nitrogen from the air in the right proportion. The pure nitrogen/hydrogen mixture passes over an iron catalyst at about 450 °C. The pressure is often about 70–200 times normal atmospheric pressure because this improves the yield and the rate of reaction, see Section 27.7. Even so, only about 15% of the gases are converted each time they go over the catalyst. Each time the gases are cooled, which causes the ammonia to form a liquid (under pressure) that can be drained out. The remaining gases are added to some new nitrogen/hydrogen mixture and sent over the catalyst again.

$$N_2(g) + 3H_2(g) \rightleftharpoons 2NH_3(g)$$

In the laboratory, ammonia can be made by heating any ammonium salt with any alkali, see Section 22.2(g). Gaseous ammonia can be collected by upward delivery, see Figure 18.4, or as a solution in water by the inverted funnel method, see Figure 21.3 (right hand side).

Ammonia is very soluble in water so the fountain experiment (Figure 18.2) can be done, substituting ammonia for hydrogen chloride. The gas has a strong smell and is poisonous. It is the only common gas which is alkaline. It is a weak alkali, see Chapter 22. A test for gaseous ammonia is that with the fumes from concentrated hydrochloric acid it will give a white smoke (fine particles of solid) of ammonium chloride. In solution ammonia will neutralise acids to give ammonium salts – it is vital to use an indicator (Section 21.1) to know when the reaction is complete. Ammonia solution (aqueous ammonia, ammonium hydroxide) is a very useful substance in analysis because it will form precipitates with many metallic salt solutions, see Figure 22.1.

The most important use of ammonia is making fertilisers, mainly ammonium nitrate. First half the ammonia is converted into nitric acid and then the remaining ammonia neutralises the nitric acid.

$$\text{ammonia} + \text{nitric acid} \rightarrow \text{ammonium nitrate}$$
$$NH_3(aq) + HNO_3(aq) \rightarrow NH_4NO_3(aq)$$

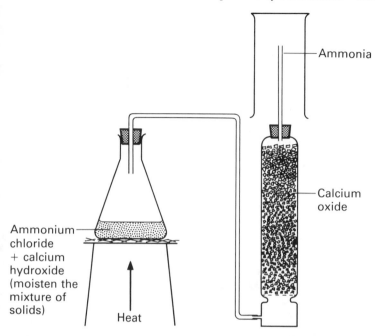

Fig. 18.4. The laboratory preparation of gaseous ammonia

Some ammonia is made into urea, which is used in plastics and as a fertiliser. Some ammonia is used to make nylon and rayon. At home, if you put a little ammonia solution into the water you will find it easier to clean the windows – it is a solvent for grease. Ammonium chloride is used in common dry cells ('batteries'), see Section 6.1, and as a flux when soldering.

18.4 Nitric acid

Nitric acid is manufactured from ammonia in three stages. First, ammonia reacts with the oxygen in air when passed over a platinum catalyst at 900 °C (Ostwald process).

$$4NH_3 + 5O_2 \rightarrow 4NO + 6H_2O$$

The nitrogen monoxide (NO) produced is cooled and then it reacts quickly with more oxygen to give nitrogen dioxide (NO_2).

$$2NO + O_2 \rightarrow 2NO_2$$

Nitrogen dioxide reacts with more oxygen and water to give concentrated nitric acid (HNO_3).

$$4NO_2 + 2H_2O + O_2 \rightarrow 4HNO_3$$

Concentrated nitric acid is a vigorous oxidising agent even when cold and is used when manufacturing nylon and Terylene. Dilute nitric acid is a typical strong acid, see Chapter 21. All nitrates are soluble in water so there is no precipitation test for a nitrate. Tests for nitrates are given in Section 38.4.

Fig. 18.5.   A fertiliser factory at Billingham (Cleveland)

Most nitric acid is made into salts, which are used as fertilisers – the nitrates of ammonia, sodium, potassium and calcium. Silver nitrate is made from nitric acid and then converted into silver bromide for photography. Nitric acid is also used to make several explosives.

18.5 Carbon dioxide

Carbon dioxide can be made in many ways. Most metal carbonates decompose when heated, except sodium carbonate and potassium carbonate, see Figure 25.3. All metal carbonates give off carbon dioxide when a dilute acid is added. This is the test for a carbonate, see Section 21.1. A typical laboratory apparatus used to prepare carbon dioxide is shown in Figure 18.6. The carbon dioxide produced can be collected over water because it is only moderately soluble. Alternatively, it can be collected by downward delivery because it is more dense than air.

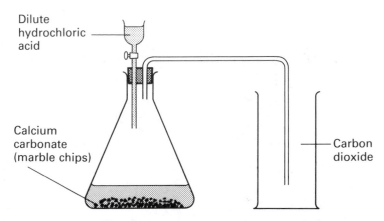

Fig. 18.6. The laboratory preparation of carbon dioxide

Carbon dioxide is produced when most fuels are burnt completely but photosynthesis converts much of it back into oxygen, see Section 7.1 and Figure 7.3. Carbon dioxide is made as a by-product in the manufacture of hydrogen (see Section 17.9) and in fermentation, see Section 19.4.

Carbon dioxide dissolved in water is a weak acid called carbonic acid, H_2CO_3. This is drunk in soda water, fizzy lemonade, beer, Coca Cola and champagne.

Solid carbon dioxide is used as a refrigerant. There is no messy liquid because it turns from solid straight into gas (sublimation) at $-78\,°C$.

Carbon dioxide will put out a burning splint or candle. Only burning magnesium is hot enough to be able to continue burning in carbon dioxide: you see the formation of a white ash of magnesium oxide and black specks of carbon and hear much spluttering. Liquid carbon dioxide under pressure is supplied in many fire extinguishers. It puts out fires by cooling and by preventing air getting to the fuel. Some fire extinguishers have a knob to strike. In these a carbonate will react with an acid: the carbon dioxide produced pushes out water to extinguish the fire.

In Magnox nuclear reactors, carbon dioxide is used to transfer the heat given out by fission reactions to water, which then is used to generate electricity. With ammonia, carbon dioxide is used to make urea. For the part carbon dioxide plays in making water temporarily hard, see Section 3.1.

Fig. 18.7. Fire extinguishers

19

Organic Compounds

19.1 Why organic?

Carbon forms more compounds than all the other elements in the periodic table put together – over 7 000 000 of them compared with just 100 000 for all the other elements. The elements in the periodic table are put into families, called groups; carbon compounds can be put into families called **homologous series**. In a homologous series of compounds the members have the same general formula, their atoms are arranged in similar patterns, they are made by similar methods and have similar physical and chemical properties. The alkanes are one example of a homologous series; the alkenes, alcohols, carboxylic acids and esters are others.

In an organic compound the reactive parts of the molecules are atoms or groups of atoms called **functional groups**. Important functional groups are:

CH_3 a carbon atom and three hydrogen atoms – a methyl group;
C_2H_5 two carbon atoms and five hydrogen atoms – an ethyl group;
OH   an oxygen and a hydrogen atom – a hydroxyl group, as found in alcohols;
COOH   a carbon, two oxygen and a hydrogen atom – a carboxyl group as in carboxylic acids;
$C{=}C$ a pair of carbon atoms connected by a double bond, as in alkenes.

At first chemists thought that there was some 'vital force' present in many carbon compounds. It is true that all living things are made up of carbon compounds, mineral salts and water, and nearly all of them breathe air, but no vital force has been found. We keep the title 'organic' for the majority of carbon compounds, except for carbon dioxide, carbon monoxide and the carbonates, which are part of inorganic chemistry.

What makes carbon so different? More than any other element its atoms can join in chains and rings. There may be double or even treble bonds between the atoms. Organic compounds often contain hydrogen, oxygen, sulphur, nitrogen and phosphorus with the carbon. Most of these compounds are covalent but the acids are partly ionic. Organic compounds are often less stable to heat than inorganic compounds. They are often flammable because of the high proportion of carbon and hydrogen in them.

19.2 The alkanes

The distillation of oil gives fractions, which are mixtures of many alkanes, see Section 5.3. Further distillation can separate the individual compounds. The general formula of this homologous series of compounds is C_nH_{2n+2} and the first four members are:

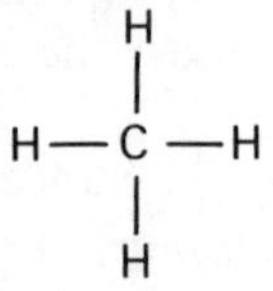

methane

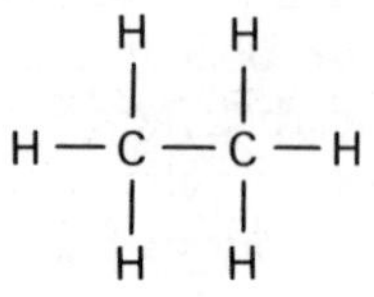

ethane

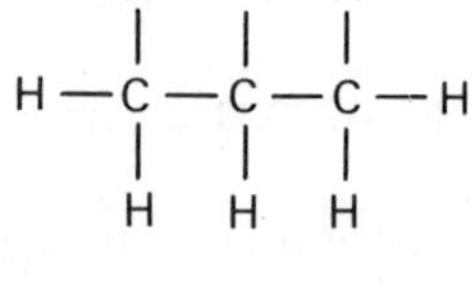

propane

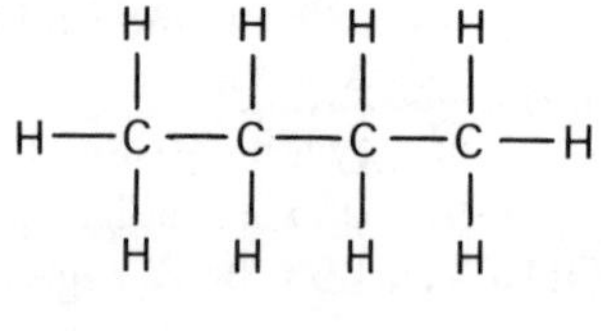

butane

The diagrams may give the impression that the molecules are flat, but the parts can twist and turn without breaking up the molecule. They are not flat but it is easier to draw them as if they are. The angle between the bonds of carbon is 109°, the angle in a tetrahedron, see Figure 31.11. Methane is the main gas in natural gas. Ethane, propane and butane are usually obtained from oil. If you like jigsaws then you will find that you can put the butane molecule together in two ways without breaking the rules of valency, see Chapter 33. The alternative structure is:

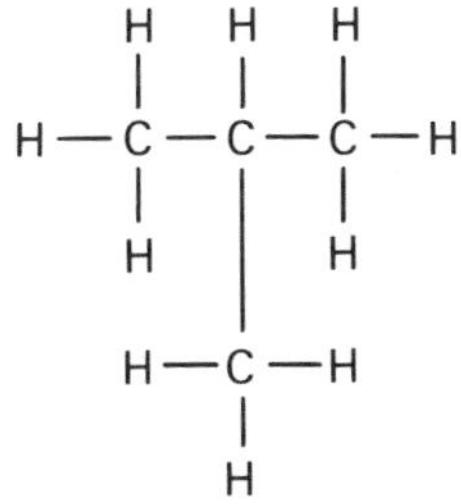

(the long bond is just for ease of drawing – it is not really any longer than the other bonds).

This form is called iso-butane or 2-methylpropane. The 2 shows that the methyl group is on the second carbon of the propane chain. The two forms are called isomers.

Isomers are substances which have the same molecular formula (the same totals of each kind of atom) **but different structural formulae** (different arrangements of the atoms).

The higher members of the alkane series, which includes octane C_8H_{18}, have plenty of isomers. Isomers of this type are very similar in their physical and chemical properties. The two butanes boil at -0.5 °C and -12 °C respectively. If the isomers are compounds in different homologous series, then there are probably a lot of differences in physical and chemical properties.

There is a slightly shorter way of writing some of these formulae without hiding their structures:

ethane CH_3CH_3 propane $CH_3CH_2CH_3$
butane $CH_3CH_2CH_2CH_3$ 2-methylpropane $CH_3CH(CH_3)CH_3$

The alkanes can be described as **saturated** compounds because each carbon atom has its maximum valency of 4. It has four atoms of hydrogen and/or carbon joined to it and it cannot join on to any more. These compounds react by **substitution**. If a hydrogen atom is removed then you can put on a chlorine or a bromine or a hydroxyl as a functional group. This can be done one or more times. For example, you can take off three of the six hydrogen atoms in ethane and put on three chlorine atoms to give you 1,1,1-trichloroethane which is a solvent for Liquid Paper and useful for degreasing (Thawpit, Genklene):

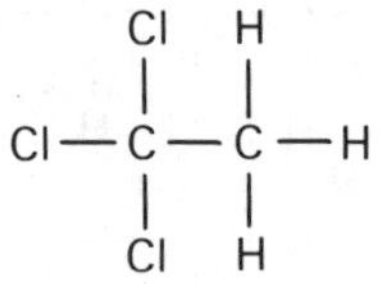

$$
\begin{array}{ccc}
& Cl & H \\
& | & | \\
Cl - & C - C & - H \\
& | & | \\
& Cl & H \\
\end{array}
$$

The 1,1,1- tells you that the three chlorine atoms are all on the first carbon atom of the ethane chain.

Three of the alkanes drawn above are used as fuel gases: methane on a large scale as natural gas; propane and the butanes in 'bottled' gas for caravans, camping and isolated houses; and butane as lighter fuel. When they burn in plenty of air they give carbon dioxide, steam and lots of energy. Methane is used to make hydrogen, see Section 17.9. Octane, the eighth member of the alkane series, used in petrol, is a liquid. The highest members are solids: you may use paraffin wax in some experiments.

19.3 The alkenes

The alkenes are a homologous series of compounds of general formula C_nH_{2n} and the first two members are:

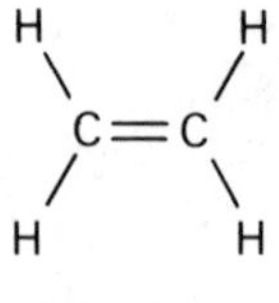

$$
\begin{array}{cc}
H \qquad\qquad H \\
\diagdown \qquad \diagup \\
C = C \\
\diagup \qquad \diagdown \\
H \qquad\qquad H \\
\end{array}
$$

or $CH_2 = CH_2$

ethene
(ethylene)

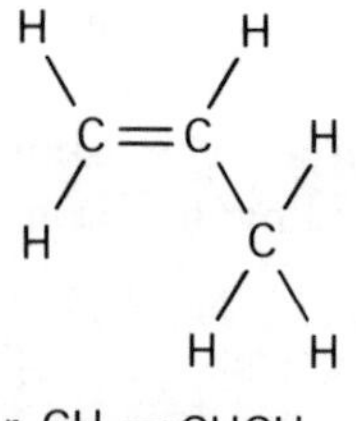

$$
\begin{array}{cc}
H \qquad\qquad H \\
\diagdown \qquad \diagup \\
C = C \quad H \\
\diagup \qquad \diagdown \diagup \\
H \qquad\qquad C \\
\diagup \diagdown \\
H \quad H \\
\end{array}
$$

or $CH_2 = CHCH_3$

propene
(propylene)

The most important part of these molecules is the double bond between two of the carbon atoms. These molecules are **unsaturated** and they react by **addition**: hydrogen and other atoms can be added to the two carbon atoms which are linked by the double bond. The double bond becomes a single bond.

In industry alkenes are made by catalytic cracking, see Section 5.3. Whenever a large saturated molecule is split up, a smaller saturated molecule and also an unsaturated molecule are produced, for example:

$$C_{10}H_{22} \rightarrow C_8H_{18} + C_2H_4$$
decane octane ethene

There are two tests to distinguish between alkanes and alkenes. In both of them alkanes do not react but alkenes do. The first test is to shake the compound with bromine water: the orange-red colour rapidly disappears if the compound is an alkene. The second test is to shake the compound with potassium manganate(VII) solution containing some sodium carbonate. If the purple colour rapidly disappears the compound is an alkene.

In both these tests the alkene molecule adds on other atoms. In the first test a bromine atom adds on to one carbon atom and a hydroxyl group to the second. The product is colourless and stays in solution. In the second test a visible product is the brown precipitate of manganese(IV) oxide. The colourless product in solution, if ethene is used, has hydroxyl groups added on to both atoms; it is called ethane-1,2-diol:

$$\begin{array}{ccc} & H & H \\ & | & | \\ H - & C - C & - H \\ & | & | \\ & OH & OH \end{array}$$

Ethane-1,2-diol, often known as ethylene glycol, is the substance used as anti-freeze in car radiators. Industry has easier and cheaper ways of making it on a large scale.

An alternative to bromine water is to use bromine dissolved in 1,1,1-trichloroethane. On shaking this solution with an alkene the red-brown colour rapidly disappears leaving a colourless solution of 1,2-dibromoethane.

$$\underset{H}{\overset{H}{\diagdown}}C=C\underset{H}{\overset{H}{\diagup}} \quad + \ Br_2 \quad \longrightarrow \quad H-\underset{\underset{Br}{|}}{\overset{\overset{H}{|}}{C}}-\underset{\underset{Br}{|}}{\overset{\overset{H}{|}}{C}}-H$$

This reaction, which can be called bromination, gives 1,2-dibromoethane, as shown above. This is added to petrol that has lead compounds in it to make sure that the lead is removed from inside the car engine.

Industry makes ethanol from ethene by passing ethene and steam at high pressure over phosphoric acid as a catalyst at 300 °C. This is an addition reaction like the two tests for alkenes described above. The double bond between two carbon atoms breaks, leaving a single bond, and the atoms making up water add on to the two carbon atoms. This reaction is an example of hydration, adding on water.

$$\underset{H}{\overset{H}{\diagdown}}C=C\underset{H}{\overset{H}{\diagup}} \quad + \ H_2O \quad \longrightarrow \quad H-\underset{\underset{H}{|}}{\overset{\overset{H}{|}}{C}}-\underset{\underset{H}{|}}{\overset{\overset{H}{|}}{C}}-OH$$

If an alkene and hydrogen are passed over a nickel catalyst at 300 °C then an alkane is produced. So ethene gives ethane.

$$\underset{H}{\overset{H}{\diagdown}}C=C\underset{H}{\overset{H}{\diagup}} \quad + \ H_2 \quad \longrightarrow \quad H-\underset{\underset{H}{|}}{\overset{\overset{H}{|}}{C}}-\underset{\underset{H}{|}}{\overset{\overset{H}{|}}{C}}-H$$

This reaction is a simple example of hydrogenation, see also Sections 17.9 and 19.6.

Ethene is used to speed up the ripening of fruit. For the polymerisation of ethene and propene, see Section 20.1.

19.4 Ethanol

Ethanol ('alcohol') is manufactured from ethene. This is done on a large scale because the pure substance is needed as a solvent and as a chemical reagent in industry. Even more ethanol is made by fermentation when making wine, beer and lager. These are all aqueous solutions which contain many other substances giving each a unique flavour. Enzymes in yeast are naturally occurring catalysts. They speed up the reaction of sugars and starches to form ethanol and carbon dioxide, for example from glucose:

glucose $\rightarrow$ ethanol $\quad$ + carbon dioxide

$C_6H_{12}O_6(aq) \rightarrow 2C_2H_5OH(aq) + 2CO_2(g)$

Even in breadmaking this reaction occurs to some extent, but by the time the loaf has been cooked the ethanol has probably evaporated or reacted elsewhere. The carbon dioxide gas makes the bread dough rise.

The concentration of ethanol in beer and cider is about 5–10%, in table wines 10–15% and in spirits about 35–40%. Drinks frequently make you a little more talkative and you feel happier because the ethanol has repressed some of your inhibitions, but too much can be disastrous. If you drink too much ethanol your liver stops working. The families of heavy drinkers and alcoholics have a very rough time. It is illegal to drive a vehicle if the concentration of ethanol in your blood is more than 80 mg/100 ml or in your breath is 35 μg/100 ml, but some people are affected by a smaller amount of alcohol than others.

When converting wines to spirits some of the water is separated out of the mixture by distillation. There is a huge wine surplus in the world and so some of it is distilled to separate the ethanol: there is a limit to the process, and you end up with a mixture of 96% ethanol and 4% water, called rectified spirit. To make industrial methylated spirit, ethanol is mixed with a more poisonous alcohol called methanol (CH_3OH). As a warning, a purple dye is added when it is sold in shops.

Ethanol can be used as a fuel because it has a low boiling point (78 °C) and it burns readily in an exothermic reaction:

$$C_2H_5OH(l) + 3O_2(g) \rightarrow 2CO_2(g) + 3H_2O(l);$$
$$\Delta H = -1372 \text{ kJ/mol}$$

In Brazil many cars are run on ethanol made by fermentation and distillation. Ethanol can be added to petrol without having to modify the car engine, see Section 26.1.

Fig. 19.1.   Distillation in large copper vessels to make whisky

Atmospheric oxidation of ethanol in drinks makes them go sour. The ethanol is converted to ethanoic acid (CH_3COOH). The 'wine vinegar' used in cooking is a mixture of ethanol and ethanoic acid.

19.5 Ethanoic acid

Ethanoic acid is often called acetic acid. A dilute solution is known as vinegar (1 mol/l); caramel is often added to give it a brown colour. Ethanoic acid is a typical weak acid, see Chapter 21. Its structure is

$$H-\underset{\underset{H}{|}}{\overset{\overset{H}{|}}{C}}-C\underset{O-H}{\overset{\diagup\!\!\!\!O}{}}$$

which can be written CH_3COOH. It is a *monobasic* acid because only the hydrogen atom attached to the oxygen atom can be replaced by a metal atom.

As vinegar, ethanoic acid is a preservative for food. It is used to give a sharp taste to fish and chips.

19.6 Esters

When an alcohol reacts with an acid, an ester and water are produced. Many esters are sweet smelling liquids. They are used as flavouring essences in cooking and as perfumes. Many of the fats that you eat are esters – beef fat, mutton fat and butter. Many vegetable oils are unsaturated esters: they may have several carbon atoms joined by double bonds in the molecule. When making fats only some of these atoms joined by double bonds may be hydrogenated, see Section 17.9. Look at the side of a packet of margarine to see if it is high in polyunsaturates.

Fig. 19.2. A well-known margarine

Soap is made from some esters by boiling them with sodium hydroxide solution. Soap (sodium octadecanoate or sodium stearate) is the sodium salt of an organic acid with a long carbon chain. The long carbon chain part dissolves in grease and the sodium carboxyl part dissolves in water, so grease and water mix together when you wash. Glycerol, commonly called glycerine, is the alcohol made from these esters at the same time as soap. It is used to make varnishes, explosives and some resins.

20

Plastics and Fibres

20.1 Addition polymerisation

The double bond in alkenes makes them more reactive than
alkanes. The single molecules are called **monomers**. They will join,
end to end, in long strings giving large molecules called **polymers**.
There are two ways of making ethene polymerise to give
poly(ethene), often called polythene.

The first way was discovered by Eric Fawcett and Reginald
Gibson in the UK in 1933: at 1500 times normal pressure and 200 °C
in the presence of a trace of oxygen, ethene gives low density
poly(ethene). This is the common form of poly(ethene). There are
molecules of many sizes, so that it does not have a definite melting
point but softens at about 90 °C. There are minor reactions which
cause molecules to have side-chains but the most important reactions follow the pattern shown in Figure 20.1. The side-chains
(not shown) cause this form of polythene to have the low density of
0·92 g/ml, so it floats on water.

The second way was discovered in 1953 by Karl Ziegler (1898–
1973, Germany). It is a low-pressure method (up to ten times
normal pressure) which can be done at room temperature or up to
70 °C. This method uses a complex catalyst of titanium and
aluminium compounds dissolved in heptane (C_7H_{16}). This gives a
poly(ethene) of higher density, 0·96 g/ml, because it has fewer and
shorter side-chains on the molecules. It softens at about 105 °C, so it
can be sterilised safely.

In the chain molecules of poly(ethene) 1000 of the monomer
molecules may join together. What is at the ends of the chains is not

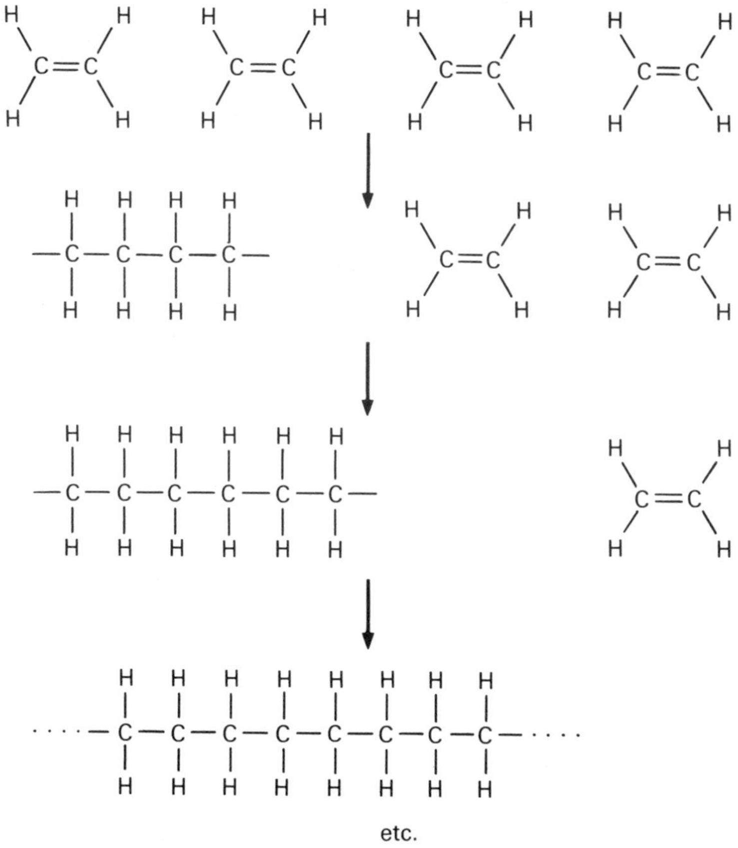

Fig. 20.1. Making ethene monomers into poly(ethene), the polymer

really important. The process is called addition polymerisation because many molecules of one compound add together to give the giant molecule. The ratio of carbon atoms to hydrogen atoms does not alter in the reaction. The polymer formed is an alkane because it does not contain any carbon atoms joined by double bonds. It is a saturated compound and unreactive except if burnt.

Many polymers are called plastics because they soften rather than melt when heated. Poly(ethene) is thermoplastic and can be moulded into various shapes or rolled into flexible sheets. The clingfilm that you use to wrap foods has a lot of other substances mixed in it to make it very flexible: it clings because of surface tension. Many of the 'ordinary' plastics you use are thinned slightly with other substances to make them cheaper and more flexible. Most polymers will not rot if they are left out in the air: they are not biodegradable and so can be a litter problem. A new type of carrier bag uses starch to hold the plastic together. If it is buried in soil it will gradually disintegrate into millions of tiny fragments.

The second way of making ethene into poly(ethene) will also work for many other substances that contain atoms joined by double bonds. Chloroethene, $CH_2{=}CHCl$, can be made into poly(chloroethene), often called PVC because its other name is polyvinyl chloride. The polymer has this structure:

$$-\underset{\underset{\displaystyle H}{|}}{\overset{\overset{\displaystyle H}{|}}{C}}-\underset{\underset{\displaystyle Cl}{|}}{\overset{\overset{\displaystyle H}{|}}{C}}-\underset{\underset{\displaystyle H}{|}}{\overset{\overset{\displaystyle H}{|}}{C}}-\underset{\underset{\displaystyle Cl}{|}}{\overset{\overset{\displaystyle H}{|}}{C}}-\qquad \text{PVC}$$

The manufacture of this polymer uses a very large amount of chlorine. It is used for artificial leather, floor tiles, gutters and pipes. If it is burnt it gives hydrogen chloride which will pollute the air.

Propene can be polymerised to give poly(propene). This is the plastic with the lowest density, 0·91 g/ml, but it has a high softening point, 145 °C. The polymer has the structure:

$$-\underset{\underset{\displaystyle H}{|}}{\overset{\overset{\displaystyle H}{|}}{C}}-\underset{\underset{\displaystyle CH_3}{|}}{\overset{\overset{\displaystyle H}{|}}{C}}-\underset{\underset{\displaystyle H}{|}}{\overset{\overset{\displaystyle H}{|}}{C}}-\underset{\underset{\displaystyle CH_3}{|}}{\overset{\overset{\displaystyle H}{|}}{C}}-\qquad \text{poly(propene)}$$

As a fibre it is used for carpets and string. Poly(propene) is also used for tent pegs and milk crates. Propene can be used to make another alkene which can be polymerised to give 'acrylic' fibres and these fibres can be used directly for fabrics or made into carbon fibres. Carbon fibres are amazingly strong: they are added to other plastics or low-density metals to give them extra strength without increasing the density too much.

Polystyrene is made by addition polymerisation. In its expanded form it is used for heat and sound insulation – cups, refrigerators and ceiling tiles. Styrene is used with a double alkene, butadiene, to make synthetic rubber.

Perspex belongs to this family of polymers. It was discovered by Rowland Hill (1904–71, England) and John Crawford in 1932. It is a better transmitter of light than glass. You find it used for illuminated road signs and round car side-lights and indicator lights.

Tetrafluoroethene, C_2F_4, polymerises to give 'PTFE'. This is a very slippery plastic which is used in non-stick pans, in moulds for tyres and in some curtain rails.

All these polymers have many trade names and sometimes it is not easy to tell which is which. Their manufacture depends on the supply of oil. Will we be in difficulties in 50 years' time? Will we have to go back to using iron and other substances if the age of plastics ends? At the moment we often use plastics because they do not rust. They are strong enough for many purposes. They are cheaper to manufacture and make into the required shape than metals. They are harder-wearing than cloth.

Fig. 20.2. Common objects made of plastics

20.2 Condensation polymerisation

Terylene is an ester which is a giant molecule. It was discovered by John Whinfield (1901–66, England) and J. T. Dickson in 1941. The name is made from the old names of its parts: terephthalic acid and ethylene glycol. It is made by a process called condensation polymerisation. It is used as a fibre.

Nylon is another fibre made by condensation polymerisation, although it is not an ester. It was discovered by Wallace Carothers (1896–1937, USA) in 1937. The name is made up from 'New York' and 'London'. Nylon is used as a fibre and also as a thermoplastic for making small gear wheels and curtain hooks.

In both of these polymers bonds are made between monomers by taking hydrogen from one molecule and hydroxyl (hydrogen and oxygen, HO) from another. The water formed is the condensation part of the name. The ratio of carbon atoms to hydrogen atoms changes as a result of polymerisation. A pictorial representation of the formation of a condensation polymer molecule is shown in Figure 20.3. The two monomer molecules alternate in the chain.

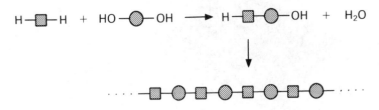

Fig. 20.3.   A condensation polymer molecule

Synthetic fibres are now used more than wool and cotton: they are better than natural fibres in their crease resistance, water repellency and strength.

20.3 Thermosets

The opposite type of plastic to a thermoplastic is a thermoset. This gets *harder* when heated, because more and more molecules join together. Examples are Bakelite, as used in light switches, and Melamine, as used in crockery, see Figure 20.4.

Fig. 20.4. A common object made from a thermoset

21

Acids

21.1 Kitchen and garden chemistry

Try sucking a lemon. You will find it tastes sour because it contains
an acid. Leave some wine out in the open for a few days: it will taste
sour. If you look in the pantry you might find some wine vinegar,
which is wine which has been partly changed to vinegar by oxidation. In summer if you leave the milk or butter out of the fridge
they will go sour: again oxidation of organic molecules gives acids.

There are coloured substances in many flowers and vegetables.
Acids may change the colours of these plants; alkalis (their chemical
opposites) change the colours differently. You can try rose petals,
blackberries, red cabbage, bluebells and so on. The coloured
substances in these plants are called **indicators** because they show
whether solutions are acidic or alkaline. Rhododendrons and many
other flowers and plants change their colour according to the acidity
of the soil. In the laboratory you may use litmus, which is made from
the bark of a tree.

Acids will corrode metals. At the start the attack may only affect
the surface of the metal but slowly the metal may dissolve completely. If the attack is fast you will see bubbles of gas (a fizz or
effervescence): the gas is hydrogen. A safe way of testing for
hydrogen is to trap some in a test tube and put a lighted splint to the
open end of the tube: you will get a 'pop', a small explosion, see
Figure 21.1.

Acids will also dissolve chalk (limestone or marble) and react
with baking powder and washing soda. These substances belong to a
class of substances called the carbonates. When acids attack them
they give off carbon dioxide gas. The fizz of mineral waters, Coca

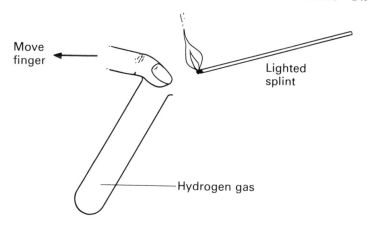

Fig. 21.1. Testing for hydrogen

Cola, beer and champagne is caused by this gas escaping from the solution into which it was forced under pressure. There are some medicines which also produce this gas when added to water: Eno's salts, Andrews' salts and some brands of soluble aspirin and vitamin C. The test for carbon dioxide is to pass the gas into calcium hydroxide solution (limewater). The clear, colourless solution goes cloudy (milky, chalky, turbid) because it becomes a fine suspension of calcium carbonate, see Figure 21.2. For further details, see Section 16.4.

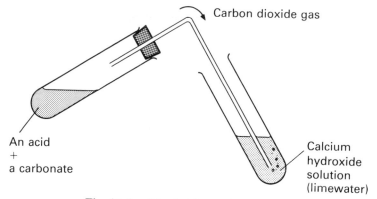

Fig. 21.2. Testing for carbon dioxide

An alternative is to use a teat pipette to suck up the gas above the bubbling solution and to squirt the gas out into the limewater.

21.2 The mineral acids

If you burn sulphur it gives sulphur dioxide. It is a very smelly experiment, best done in a fume cupboard. Sulphur dioxide is very soluble in water, giving **sulphurous acid** (H_2SO_3). This acid, or substances made from it, is used to prevent jam and fruit going mouldy. It is easily oxidised to sulphuric acid (H_2SO_4).

In industry sulphur dioxide is made in two stages into **sulphuric acid**, see Section 18.2. Sulphuric acid, H_2SO_4, was the first acid made from naturally occurring minerals. Concentrated sulphuric acid is a very dangerous liquid so you must be very careful if you are using it.

If concentrated sulphuric acid is poured on to sodium chloride crystals (common salt) the gas hydrogen chloride, HCl, is released. The gas can be dissolved in water by the inverted funnel method, see Figure 21.3. The solution is called **hydrochloric acid**. The funnel must only just dip into the water in the beaker. The crystals left in the flask are still acidic – they are sodium hydrogensulphate, which is used in some toilet cleaners.

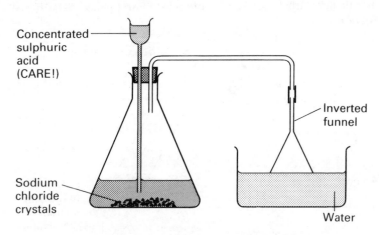

Concentrated sulphuric acid (CARE!)

Inverted funnel

Sodium chloride crystals

Water

Fig. 21.3. Making hydrochloric acid

The third mineral acid is **nitric acid**, HNO_3. It can be made by heating concentrated sulphuric acid with sodium nitrate in an all-glass apparatus. Concentrated nitric acid is another very dangerous liquid. Industry makes nitric acid from ammonia, air and water, see Section 18.4.

These three mineral acids, even when in dilute solution (up to 30% by mass in water), show the same sort of properties as lemon juice and vinegar. The chemical similarity is that all the acids contain hydrogen atoms which can be replaced by metal atoms, forming salts.

The basicity of an acid is the number of hydrogen atoms in one molecule of an acid which can be replaced by metal atoms.

Hydrochloric acid, HCl, is monobasic; so is nitric acid, HNO_3. Sulphuric acid, H_2SO_4, is dibasic. Acetic or ethanoic acid is only monobasic, even though its formula is $H_4C_2O_2$. Only one of its hydrogen atoms can be replaced. Phosphoric acid, H_3PO_4, is tribasic: its salts are used in Coca Cola.

21.3 Water is vital for acidity

Dry litmus paper is not affected by dry hydrogen chloride gas. Wet litmus paper will change from blue to red if put in hydrogen chloride. Also if dry blue litmus paper is put in hydrochloric acid (hydrogen chloride in water), it will change to red.

Sulphuric acid and nitric acid are liquids but they do not act as acids unless they are mixed with water. Without water, or in concentrated solution, they have other and more dangerous properties such as being powerful oxidising agents.

Baking powder, soluble aspirin and soluble vitamin C are all mixtures of acids and carbonates. You can safely keep them in a tin or bottle because there is no water. When they are added to water the carbonates react with the acids giving carbon dioxide. Acid behaviour is only shown when there is water present. The acids if dry are covalent; in water they are ionic. When hydrogen chloride is dissolved in methylbenzene and when citric acid is dissolved in propanone they are not acidic because in these solvents they are covalent. So the best definition of an acid is as follows.

An acid is a substance which in water gives hydrogen ions as the only positive ions. (An acid is a proton donor.)

The word 'only' in the definition is vital to exclude substances such as sodium hydrogensulphate, $NaHSO_4$, which gives Na^+, H^+, HSO_4^- and SO_4^{2-} ions. This is an 'acid salt', see Section 23.7.

Strong acids are mostly ionised in solution; weak acids are only partly ionised. The three mineral acids are strong acids but acetic acid and citric acid are weak acids.

21.4 The properties of an acid

(*a*) *Taste*　Acids taste sour, but some are poisonous or very corrosive. Do **not** try this test unless given permission.

(*b*) *Indicators*　To be sure that you have an acid you must see the indicator change its colour.

　　Litmus: blue turns to red

　　Phenolphthalein: red turns colourless

　　Methyl orange: yellow turns red

(*c*) *Metals*　Many metals will dissolve in many acids. Some metals are so reactive in water that it might be dangerous to use an acid. You can try calcium, magnesium, aluminium, zinc or iron with dilute hydrochloric acid or dilute sulphuric acid. Hydrogen is produced in most of these cases and can be confirmed by the 'pop' test. The general equation for the reaction is:

$$\text{metal} + \text{acid} \rightarrow \text{salt} + \text{hydrogen}$$

Copper does not react with dilute hydrochloric acid or dilute sulphuric acid.

(*d*) *Metal oxides*　Many metal oxides will dissolve in many acids. For example, the black solid copper(II) oxide dissolves in warm dilute sulphuric acid to give a blue solution of copper(II) sulphate. The general equation is:

$$\text{metal oxide} + \text{acid} \rightarrow \text{salt} + \text{water}$$

(*e*) *Metal hydroxides*　Many metal hydroxides will dissolve in many acids. For example, the white solid zinc hydroxide dissolves in dilute nitric acid to give a colourless solution of zinc nitrate. The general equation is:

metal hydroxide + acid → salt + water

For more details see Sections 23.3 and 23.4.

(*f*) *Metal carbonates* Many metal carbonates will dissolve in many acids. For example, calcium carbonate (chalk, limestone, marble) will dissolve in dilute hydrochloric acid to give a colourless solution of calcium chloride and carbon dioxide which bubbles off. You can test the gas with limewater. The general equation is:

metal carbonate + acid → salt + water + carbon dioxide

For more details see Sections 23.3 to 23.6.

21.5 The pH scale

Most indicators show only two colours: one for an acidic solution, another for an alkaline solution. By mixing several simple indicators you can make a 'universal' indicator that shows a range of colours. For example, a mixture of methyl orange, methyl red, bromothymol blue and phenolphthalein in alcohol and water will show a range of colour from red to green to violet (a spectrum) according to the concentration of acid or alkali to which it is added, see Figure 21.4.

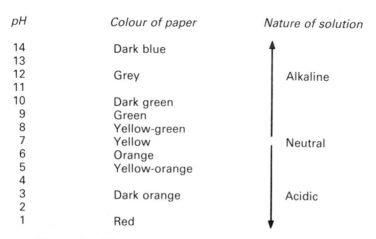

pH	Colour of paper	Nature of solution
14	Dark blue	
13		
12	Grey	Alkaline
11		
10	Dark green	
9	Green	
8	Yellow-green	
7	Yellow	Neutral
6	Orange	
5	Yellow-orange	
4		
3	Dark orange	Acidic
2		
1	Red	

Fig. 21.4. The colour of pH paper in acids and alkalis

The pH scale is a numerical way of saying how acidic or alkaline a solution is. The colours of a universal indicator solution or of pH paper can be translated into numbers:

(*a*) From 0 up to 6 means an acidic solution; the lower the number, the more acidic the solution is.
(*b*) Precisely 7 means a neutral solution.
(*c*) From 8 up to 14 means an alkaline solution; the higher the number, the more alkaline the solution.

Freshly distilled water has a pH of 7 at room temperature. Rainwater has a pH less than 7 because it contains dissolved carbon dioxide, and usually sulphur dioxide and oxides of nitrogen as well. The pH of your gastric juices is about 1 because of the hydrochloric acid in your stomach. Most of the food you eat and the liquids you drink are neutral or slightly acidic.

If you use a universal indicator or pH paper you can study the change in pH as you do a titration. At the start there is hardly any change, around the end-point ('neutralisation') there is a rapid change, and finally there is hardly any change, see Figure 21.5.

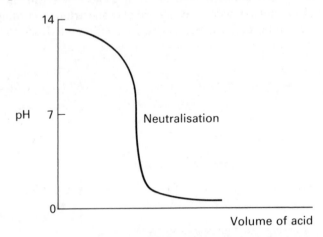

Fig. 21.5.   The alteration in pH when a strong acid is added to a strong alkali in titration

22

Bases (Alkalis)

22.1 Is it soluble in water?

Bases are a large class of compounds, which includes metal oxides and metal hydroxides. Most of these compounds are insoluble in water. Alkalis are a small section of this class: they are soluble in water. Only alkalis will change the colours of indicators and so they are easily recognised.

Litmus: red turns blue
Phenolphthalein: colourless turns red
Methyl orange: red turns yellow

Strong alkalis are mostly ionised; weak alkalis are only partly ionised. Sodium hydroxide and potassium hydroxide are strong alkalis; ammonia dissolved in water is a weak alkali. Ammonia solution is unstable and has a strong smell. Calcium hydroxide is a strong alkali but it is not very soluble in water and so it is not as corrosive as sodium hydroxide and potassium hydroxide.

A base is a substance which will react with an acid to give a salt and water only. (A base is a proton acceptor.)

An alkali is a soluble base.

The reaction of a base with an acid is called a **neutralisation**: the hydrogen ions of the acid are replaced by metal ions. For example,

$$Ca(OH)_2 + 2HNO_3 \rightarrow Ca(NO_3)_2 + 2H_2O$$

The general equation is:

$$\text{acid} + \text{base} \rightarrow \text{salt} + \text{water}$$

and the ionic equation is always:

$$H^+(aq) + OH^-(aq) \rightarrow H_2O(l)$$

22.2 The properties of a base

(a) *Corrosion*   If you are working with sodium hydroxide (or potassium hydroxide) solution you must wear your safety spectacles. These two alkalis will corrode you (they are caustic, that is to say burning), your papers and your clothes as well as make a mark on the bench. A dilute solution of sodium hydroxide feels soapy because it is reacting with the fat of your skin, see (*e*).

(b) *Indicators*   Only alkalis, the soluble bases, affect indicators.

(c) *Acids*   Acids react with bases to give salts and water only. The general equations are as follows:

$$\text{metal oxide} \qquad + \text{ acid } \rightarrow \text{ salt} + \text{water}$$
$$\text{metal hydroxide} + \text{ acid } \rightarrow \text{ salt} + \text{water}$$

Metal carbonates behave in a very similar way but also give carbon dioxide:

$$\text{metal carbonate} + \text{acid} \rightarrow \text{salt} + \text{water} + \text{carbon dioxide}$$

For more details see Sections 23.3 to 23.6.

(d) *Metals*   The caustic alkalis will corrode a few metals, such as aluminium and zinc. The metal becomes part of an anion and hydrogen is released. The equations are complex but follow the pattern:

$$\text{metal} + \text{alkali} \rightarrow \text{complex salt} + \text{hydrogen}$$

Sodium carbonate (washing soda) solution is slightly alkaline in solution. It should not be used when cleaning an aluminium pan because it will spoil the surface.

(e) *Fats and oils*   Many of these are esters, see Section 19.6. They are saponified (made into soap) by caustic alkalis:

$$\text{fat or oil} + \text{caustic alkali} \rightarrow \text{soap} + \text{glycerol (glycerine)}$$

(*f*) *Metal salts* Most metal salts in solution will react with alkalis. It does not matter whether the metal salt is a chloride, a nitrate or a sulphate as long as it is soluble in water. If you use sodium hydroxide solution you *may* get a different result from using ammonia solution. The results are very useful in analysis when you want to find the cation or metallic part of a salt in an unknown compound. Salts of group I metals do not give precipitates (insoluble products) with sodium hydroxide or ammonia solution. In all other cases you look for the formation of a precipitate, what colour it is and whether it dissolves if excess alkali is used, see Figure 22.1.

(*g*) *Ammonium salts* The caustic alkalis will react with ammonium salts to give ammonia gas. For example,

sodium + ammonium → sodium + water + ammonia
  hydroxide chloride   chloride

$NaOH(aq) + NH_4Cl(aq) \rightarrow NaCl(aq) + H_2O(l) + NH_3(g)$

Group	Metal in a solution of a salt	With sodium hydroxide solution		With ammonia solution	
		at first	*in excess*	*at first*	*in excess*
II	magnesium	white precipitate	no change	white precipitate	no change
	calcium	white precipitate	no change	no precipitate	no precipitate
III	aluminium	white precipitate	colourless solution	white precipitate	no change
IV	lead(II)	white precipitate	colourless solution	white precipitate	no change
d-block	iron(II)	green precipitate	no change	green precipitate	no change
	iron(III)	red-brown precipitate	no change	red-brown precipitate	no change
	copper(II)	pale blue precipitate	no change	pale blue precipitate	deep blue solution
	zinc	white precipitate	colourless solution	white precipitate	colourless solution

Fig. 22.1. Precipitation tests with alkalis

It may be necessary for the mixture to be warmed very carefully for the reaction to occur. The tests for ammonia are

   (i) litmus – it is the only alkaline gas you will meet at this stage;
  (ii) it has a strong smell;
 (iii) with concentrated hydrochloric acid (a drop on the end of a glass rod) it will form a white smoke of ammonium chloride.

22.3 Amphoteric substances

There are a few metal hydroxides which will dissolve in acids and also in caustic alkalis. These metal hydroxides are **amphoteric**. The amphoteric nature of these substances is also found in the metals and their oxides. Zinc hydroxide, aluminium hydroxide and lead(II) hydroxide are the best examples. Notice that these metals are all close to the metal/non-metal boundary in the periodic table. Equations for some reactions are as follows:

zinc hydroxide   +   hydrochloric acid $\rightarrow$ zinc chloride   + water

$Zn(OH)_2(s)$ + $2HCl(aq)$ $\rightarrow$ $ZnCl_2(aq)$ + $2H_2O(l)$

Zinc hydroxide   +   sodium hydroxide $\rightarrow$ sodium zincate

$Zn(OH)_2(s)$ + $2NaOH(aq)$ $\rightarrow$ $Na_2Zn(OH)_4(aq)$

22.4 Indigestion remedies

In your stomach you have a very dilute solution of hydrochloric acid and enzymes (natural substances which are catalysts). These give the right conditions for food to be broken down into smaller molecules which are then carried round in your bloodstream to various parts of your body. Sometimes indigestion is caused by too much hydrochloric acid being produced. The aim of an indigestion remedy is to neutralise the excess acid. You don't want your stomach juices to become alkaline because that would be just as painful. Many remedies for indigestion are of these two types.

(*a*) Compounds which have a very low solubility, such as magnesium hydroxide and sodium hydrogencarbonate. The first is sold as a powder suspended in water – 'Milk of Magnesia':

magnesium + hydrochloric → magnesium + water
hydroxide   acid   chloride

$Mg(OH)_2$ + 2HCl(aq) → $MgCl_2$(aq) + $2H_2O$(l)
   (s and aq)

The second is sold as tablets of 'Sodamint' which you can suck so that they slowly dissolve.

sodium hydrogencarbonate + hydrochloric acid →
                 sodium chloride + water + carbon dioxide

$NaHCO_3$(aq) + HCl(aq) → NaCl(aq) + H_2O(l) + CO_2(g)

(b) Compounds which are insoluble in water, such as calcium carbonate and magnesium carbonate. Tablets of these compounds are sold as 'Rennies' and 'BiSoDol'. They fall to pieces in your mouth and you swallow the powder. In your stomach the powder reacts with the hydrochloric acid.

calcium carbonate + hydrochloric acid →
                 calcium chloride + water + carbon dioxide

$CaCO_3$(s) + 2HCl(aq) → $CaCl_2$(aq) + H_2O(l) + CO_2(g)

The only drawback to several of these remedies, as you may realise, is that the carbon dioxide bubbles off inside your stomach!

23

Salts

23.1 Making salts

A salt is produced when an acid reacts with a base. Usually water is made at the same time. A salt is a compound of a metal with any non-metal except oxygen or a hydroxide. Some examples of salts are

$NaCl$	sodium chloride, common salt
$Ca(NO_3)_2$	calcium nitrate
$CuCO_3$	copper(II) carbonate
$ZnSO_4$	zinc sulphate

The method of making a salt depends on three conditions.

(a) Is the salt stable to water? If it is unstable to water or is needed without any water of crystallisation it may have to be made by synthesis, see Section 23.2. (The reaction of a salt with water is called hydrolysis.)

(b) Is the base soluble in water, that is to say, is it an alkali? If the base is soluble you can do a titration, see Section 23.3. If the base is insoluble in water you must follow the method in Section 23.4.

(c) Is the salt you want insoluble in water? If the base you are given is soluble see Section 23.5. If the base you are given is insoluble in water see Section 23.6.

All acids are soluble in water, but there are very few alkalis, see Section 22.1. There is a summary of soluble salts in Section 13.3.

23.2 Synthesis (direct combination)

If you heat iron with sulphur you get iron(II) sulphide:

$$Fe(s) + S(s) \rightarrow FeS(s)$$

This reaction is sometimes studied to show the differences between elements, mixtures and compounds.

It is possible, by solution methods, to get crystals of iron(III) chloride-6-water, $FeCl_3 \cdot 6H_2O$, but these hydrolyse if you try to remove the water by heating them. It is important to be able to make anhydrous iron(III) chloride for use as a catalyst.

If you heat iron in a stream of dry chlorine gas you get iron(III) chloride:

$$2Fe(s) + 3Cl_2(g) \rightarrow 2FeCl_3(s)$$

The solid sublimes into a cold receiver, see Figure 23.1.

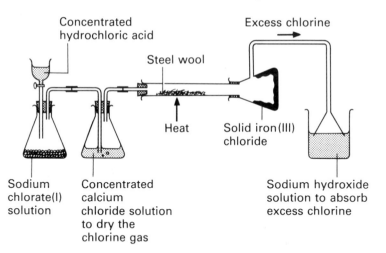

Fig. 23.1. The synthesis of iron(III) chloride

If you pass dry hydrogen chloride over hot iron you will get iron(II) chloride. Iron shows variable valency and is a typical transition element. Aluminium only shows a valency of three and so aluminium chloride, $AlCl_3$, can be made by passing dry hydrogen chloride *or* chlorine over hot aluminium.

23.3 Soluble base being made into a soluble salt

The way of doing this is the important process of titration. As well as being used to make salts, a titration can be done to measure solubility, purity or the rate of a reaction. You must be able to do a titration very accurately, so attention to detail is important. You can follow the progress of a titration by using an indicator, by measuring the electrical conductivity of the solution or even by measuring the temperature (if you do the experiment rapidly).

A **titration** is the process of adding one solution to another until

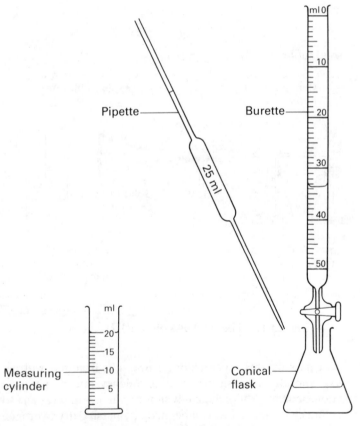

Fig. 23.2. Apparatus for a titration

the solutes have just reacted. It is often done by running an acid from a burette into an alkali, mixed with some indicator, in a conical flask, see Figure 23.2. The indicator shows you whether the solution is alkaline, neutral or acidic. The steps in the titration are as follows.

(*a*) Rinse a conical flask with water. It does not have to be dry but it must be clean.

(*b*) Rinse a measuring cylinder with water and with a little of the alkali for the experiment. Then fill the measuring cylinder up to the required volume, say 25 ml (cm^3), with the alkali. The bottom of the 'meniscus' of a solution should be just on the mark, see Figure 23.3. An alternative is to use a pipette and a safety device for sucking liquid into it. It is cleaned and used in the same way as a measuring cylinder.

(*c*) Pour the alkali from the measuring cylinder into the conical flask. Add two or three drops of a suitable indicator. Indicators have to be chosen carefully according to whether the acid is strong or weak and whether the alkali is strong or weak.

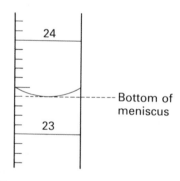

Fig. 23.3. Reading the volume on a measuring cylinder, pipette or burette. Check which mark is just touching the meniscus. Here it is 23·4 ml (cm^3)

(*d*) Rinse a burette with water and with a little of the acid for the experiment. Then fill the burette up beyond the zero mark with the acid. A plastic funnel is useful when putting water or solutions in the burette. When rinsing the burette don't forget the part below the tap. Adjust the level of the solution to be at the zero mark or at some other point on the scale, when the burette is full below the tap.

(*e*) Note the volume of acid in the burette. Run the acid slowly out into the alkali, swirling the flask to mix the solutions thoroughly. When you realise that the indicator is about to change its colour go very slowly, drop by drop. Stop the moment a definite colour change has occurred. Note the final volume of acid in the burette. Record all your readings.

Burette readings in ml	Titration 1	Titration 2	Titration 3
At the end	23·5	46·8	23·4
At the start .	0·0	23·5	0·0
Difference (titre)	23·5	23·3	23·4

Average titre = 23·4 ml

Fig. 23.4.   Titration results: 25 ml of sodium hydroxide solution with hydrochloric acid using methyl orange as the indicator

(*f*) To repeat the titration, for greater accuracy, rinse out the flask with water, put another 25 ml portion of alkali into the flask, add some indicator, put more acid in the burette if necessary and repeat (*e*). You may record your burette readings as in Figure 23.4.

   Sometimes when you do a titration you ignore the first result because you doubt its accuracy. For any calculations you take an average of the accurate titres, see Section 37.2.

(*g*) If you are doing the titration to make sodium chloride, you take 25 ml of sodium hydroxide solution and the average volume of hydrochloric acid (23·4 ml in Figure 23.4). You do not add any indicator.

(*h*) Put the solution into an evaporating basin and boil it until about half to one third is left. Then you may see some crystals starting to form so you let the solution cool slowly. Don't boil the solution dry. If you are not in a hurry let the solution evaporate for a week to get bigger crystals.

(*i*) Scrape the crystals into a filter paper in a funnel, rinse them with a little water and press them dry between new filter papers.

The equation for the reaction described above is:

$$\begin{array}{ccccc} \text{sodium} & + & \text{hydrochloric} & \rightarrow & \text{sodium} & + & \text{water} \\ \text{hydroxide} & & \text{acid} & & \text{chloride} \end{array}$$

$$\text{NaOH(aq)} + \text{HCl(aq)} \rightarrow \text{NaCl(aq)} + \text{H}_2\text{O(l)}$$

Sodium carbonate solution can be titrated in the same way as sodium hydroxide solution; methyl orange *must* be used as the indicator.

$$\text{Na}_2\text{CO}_3\text{(aq)} + 2\text{HCl(aq)} \rightarrow 2\text{NaCl(aq)} + \text{H}_2\text{O(l)} + \text{CO}_2\text{(g)}$$

23.4 Insoluble base being made into a soluble salt

The insoluble base may be a metal oxide or metal hydroxide. Metals (except those too reactive for safety or copper which is unreactive) and metal carbonates (insoluble in water) can be used in the same way. Although the base is insoluble in water it is soluble in the acid. The steps in this general method of making salts are as follows.

(*a*) Put some dilute acid into a beaker. For example, you might put 50 ml of dilute sulphuric acid into a 250 ml beaker.
(*b*) Warm the acid but do not boil it.
(*c*) Add the base to the warm acid until no more of the base will dissolve in the acid. For example, you might use copper(II) oxide.
(*d*) Filter off the excess base.
(*e*) Complete the experiment as in (*h*) and (*i*) in Section 23.3.

The equation for the reaction described above is

$$\begin{array}{ccccc} \text{copper(II)} & + & \text{sulphuric} & \rightarrow & \text{copper(II)} & + & \text{water} \\ \text{oxide} & & \text{acid} & & \text{sulphate} \end{array}$$

$$\text{CuO(s)} + \text{H}_2\text{SO}_4\text{(aq)} \rightarrow \text{CuSO}_4\text{(aq)} + \text{H}_2\text{O(l)}$$

23.5 Soluble base being made into an insoluble salt

The two solutions are mixed, giving a precipitate of the insoluble salt required. This method is not limited to using a soluble base and an acid. It can be applied to any two solutions which will supply the metal (the cation) and the non-metal (the anion) of the insoluble salt that is wanted. Five examples are given.

(*a*) Calcium hydroxide solution (a soluble base, an alkali) and dilute carbonic acid when mixed give a precipitate of calcium carbonate.

$$Ca(OH)_2(aq) + H_2CO_3(aq) \rightarrow CaCO_3(s) + 2H_2O(l)$$

This equation can be simplified to:

$$Ca^{2+}(aq) + CO_3^{2-}(aq) \rightarrow CaCO_3(s)$$

(*b*) Barium chloride solution (soluble salt supplying the cation) and dilute sulphuric acid or sodium sulphate solution (soluble substances supplying the anion) when mixed give a precipitate of barium sulphate. This is the normal test for a sulphate. Some dilute hydrochloric acid is added as a precaution against other precipitates being formed.

$$BaCl_2(aq) + Na_2SO_4(aq) \rightarrow BaSO_4(s) + 2NaCl(aq)$$

This equation can be simplified to:

$$Ba^{2+}(aq) + SO_4^{2-}(aq) \rightarrow BaSO_4(s)$$

(*c*) Silver nitrate solution (soluble salt supplying the cation) and dilute hydrochloric acid or potassium chloride solution (soluble substances supplying the anion) when mixed give a precipitate of silver chloride. This is the normal test for a chloride. Some dilute nitric acid is added as a precaution against other precipitates being formed.

$$AgNO_3(aq) + KCl(aq) \rightarrow AgCl(s) + KNO_3(aq)$$

This equation can be simplified to:

$$Ag^+(aq) + Cl^-(aq) \rightarrow AgCl(s)$$

(*d*) The method also applies to the preparation of most metal carbonates using sodium carbonate solution. For example:

copper(II) sulphate	+ sodium carbonate	→ copper carbonate	+ sodium sulphate
$CuSO_4(aq)$	$+ Na_2CO_3(aq)$	$\rightarrow CuCO_3(s)$	$+ Na_2SO_4(aq)$

In all these four cases the precipitate can be collected by filtration, rinsed with water and pressed dry between new filter papers.

(*e*) When a soluble substance is wanted, you can use this method to eliminate an insoluble salt, as in the following example. Slowly add a suspension of barium peroxide in water to some ice-cold dilute sulphuric acid. Barium sulphate is precipitated and you are left with a dilute solution of hydrogen peroxide. Continue the addition until the acidity is very slight because hydrogen peroxide solution keeps best if it is slightly acidic.

23.6 Insoluble base being made into an insoluble salt

If the insoluble base is in lumps rather than a very fine powder, the only reliable way of doing this experiment is to make a soluble substance as the half-way stage. If you put calcium carbonate in the form of marble chips into dilute sulphuric acid, the reaction soon stops: the chips become covered with a film of insoluble calcium sulphate which stops the reaction. The best method is to dissolve the marble chips in dilute nitric acid or dilute hydrochloric acid.

$$CaCO_3(s) + 2HNO_3(aq) \rightarrow Ca(NO_3)_2(aq) + H_2O(l) + CO_2(g)$$

Then you add a soluble metal sulphate (or sulphuric acid) to the solution.

$$Ca(NO_3)_2(aq) + Na_2SO_4(aq) \rightarrow CaSO_4(s) + 2NaNO_3(aq)$$

Collect the precipitate by filtration, rinse it with water and press it dry between new filter papers.

23.7 Acid salts and normal salts

If you titrate sodium hydroxide solution with dilute sulphuric acid in the presence of an indicator, you can make sodium sulphate. This titration tells you the volumes of the solutions to obtain a neutral solution. Sulphuric acid, H_2SO_4, is a dibasic acid and sodium sulphate, Na_2SO_4, is a **normal salt** because both the hydrogen atoms of the acid have been replaced by sodium atoms.

$$2NaOH(aq) + H_2SO_4(aq) \rightarrow Na_2SO_4(aq) + 2H_2O(l)$$

To make an **acid salt** you can double the volume of the acid or halve the volume of the alkali. After evaporation you get crystals of sodium hydrogensulphate, $NaHSO_4$.

$$NaOH(aq) + H_2SO_4(aq) \rightarrow NaHSO_4(aq) + H_2O(l)$$

In an acid salt only some of the hydrogen atoms of the acid have been replaced by metal atoms. Sodium hydrogensulphate (note that the name of the anion is one word) when dissolved in water gives Na^+, H^+, SO_4^{2-} and HSO_4^- ions. It is acidic to litmus; it cannot be made directly by titration.

If you blow carbon dioxide gas into sodium carbonate solution then sodium hydrogencarbonate is produced. If the solution is concentrated, sodium hydrogencarbonate will form as a precipitate.

$$Na_2CO_3(aq) + H_2O(l) + CO_2(g) \rightarrow 2NaHCO_3(aq \text{ and } s)$$

Sodium hydrogencarbonate is another acid salt, but when you test its solution you find that it is alkaline. Salts are not always neutral in solution, because of hydrolysis, nor are acid salts always acidic.

Calcium hydrogencarbonate, which makes water temporarily hard, is another acid salt, see Chapter 3.

24

Oxidation and Reduction

24.1 Adding oxygen

When natural gas burns it reacts with the oxygen in the air. Natural gas, methane, is a compound of carbon and hydrogen. The carbon gains oxygen, becoming carbon dioxide. The hydrogen gains oxygen, becoming steam or water, depending on the temperature. The gas has been oxidised and its combustion (burning) releases heat to keep us warm or to cook our food.

methane $+$ oxygen $\rightarrow$ carbon dioxide $+$ water
$$CH_4(g) \quad + \; 2O_2(g) \rightarrow CO_2(g) \qquad + \; 2H_2O(l)$$

The addition of oxygen to a substance is known as oxidation. It may happen to compounds or to elements. Coke, which is made from coal, is mostly carbon; so is charcoal, made from wood. Carbon will burn in air, forming carbon dioxide. This acidic oxide makes rainwater slightly acidic.

carbon $+$ oxygen $\rightarrow$ carbon dioxide
$$C(s) \quad + \; O_2(g) \; \rightarrow CO_2(g)$$

White phosphorus is so reactive that it may catch fire spontaneously (of its own accord) in moist air. It burns to become phosphorus(V) oxide (another acidic oxide).

phosphorus $+$ oxygen $\rightarrow$ phosphorus(V) oxide
$$P_4(s) \qquad + \; 5O_2(g) \rightarrow 2P_2O_5(s)$$

Sulphur requires warming before it will burn to become sulphur dioxide. There is some sulphur in both petroleum and coal, so when these fuels are burnt some sulphur dioxide is also released into the air. Sulphur dioxide is one of the major causes of pollution of the air. It leads to 'acid rain'.

$$\text{sulphur} \quad + \quad \text{oxygen} \rightarrow \text{sulphur dioxide}$$
$$S(s) \quad + \quad O_2(g) \quad \rightarrow SO_2(g)$$

For the contribution of the oxides of nitrogen to acid rain see Section 1.3.

24.2 Recycling the oxygen

If air is in short supply when fuels are burnt there is the danger of making carbon monoxide.

$$\text{carbon} + \text{oxygen} \rightarrow \text{carbon monoxide}$$
$$2C(s) \quad + \quad O_2(g) \quad \rightarrow 2CO(g)$$

The carburettor in your car mixes petrol vapour with air in the best possible way but a car exhaust still contains about 2% carbon monoxide. It is not safe to run a car engine in a garage with the doors shut. People who smoke tobacco and people close to them also get some carbon monoxide in their blood. The red blood cells cannot carry oxygen as a result. When dealing with a big fire the firemen will wear breathing apparatus, carrying their own air supply, to protect themselves against carbon monoxide and smoke. Too much carbon monoxide will cause death. Out in the fresh air, sunlight will help oxygen to combine with carbon monoxide to make carbon dioxide. Thus oxidation can occur in stages: carbon → carbon monoxide → carbon dioxide.

$$\text{carbon monoxide} \quad + \quad \text{oxygen} \rightarrow \text{carbon dioxide}$$
$$2CO(g) \quad + \quad O_2(g) \quad \rightarrow 2CO_2(g)$$

Every year we burn billions of tonnes of the fossil fuels, gas, coal and petroleum. We still have plenty of oxygen in the air because plants regain the oxygen by photosynthesis, see Section 7.1.

$$\text{carbon dioxide} + \text{water} \quad \rightarrow \text{glucose} \quad + \text{oxygen}$$
$$6CO_2(g) \quad + \quad 6H_2O(l) \rightarrow C_6H_{12}O_6(s) \quad + \quad 6O_2(g)$$

The equation conceals the experimental fact that all the oxygen released comes from the carbon dioxide. Radioactive substances were used to follow the route of this reaction, which occurs in many stages. By using radioactive carbon (half life 5570 years, see Section 28.5) we can tell if the carbon atoms present at one stage end up in one product or another.

24.3 Adding oxygen to more elements

Hydrogen and oxygen will explode if sparked or if a small flame is put to the mixture. Hydrogen will burn smoothly in oxygen if pure hydrogen comes from a jet. Hundreds of tonnes of hydrogen and oxygen are burnt in rockets so that the space shuttle can leave the earth.

Airships for passengers originally used hydrogen despite its flammability. Hydrogen, as the least dense gas, has the greatest lifting power. After the Hindenburg disaster in 1937 when many people were killed, airships went out of fashion. Today helium is used in airships. It is not quite so good for lift but it cannot be oxidised so it is safe. Hydrogen-filled balloons are still used by the weathermen and are often sold at fairs: they may be carried by the wind for many hundreds of kilometres.

Magnesium, if heated, will burn in air. The reaction gives out a lot of heat and a bright white light (take care not to look at it directly). The white powder left is magnesium oxide.

$$\text{magnesium} \ + \ \text{oxygen} \rightarrow \text{magnesium oxide}$$
$$2Mg(s) \qquad + \ O_2(g) \ \rightarrow 2MgO(s)$$

If you press this powder onto some damp red litmus paper you will find that the paper slowly turns blue. Magnesium oxide with water gives magnesium hydroxide which is alkaline. You might be given some as 'Milk of Magnesia'. Why?

$$\text{magnesium oxide} \ + \ \text{water} \ \rightarrow \text{magnesium hydroxide}$$
$$MgO(s) \qquad\qquad + \ H_2O(l) \rightarrow Mg(OH)_2(s + aq)$$

Sodium, potassium and calcium can be burnt and the compounds produced are like magnesium oxide. There are many other metals which will burn but the compounds produced do not react with water. They are insoluble bases, see Chapter 22. For example, the sparks that come from hot iron are caused by the reaction:

$$\text{iron} + \text{oxygen} \rightarrow \text{iron oxide}$$
$$3Fe(s) + 2O_2(g) \rightarrow Fe_3O_4(s)$$

The full name of this black iron oxide is iron(II) diiron(III) oxide.

Oxygen is only one of the 21 non-metals. If a metallic element or a compound combines with chlorine or sulphur or any of the other non-metals then the reaction is still called an oxidation. The reaction of magnesium with chlorine is the oxidation of magnesium in the same way as the reaction of magnesium with oxygen.

$$\text{magnesium} + \text{chlorine} \rightarrow \text{magnesium chloride}$$
$$Mg(s) + Cl_2(g) \rightarrow MgCl_2(s)$$

When a metal such as magnesium or iron dissolves in an acid, the reaction is the oxidation of the metal.

$$\text{magnesium} + \text{hydrochloric} \rightarrow \text{magnesium} + \text{hydrogen}$$
$$\text{acid} \qquad\qquad \text{chloride}$$
$$Mg(s) + 2HCl(aq) \rightarrow MgCl_2(aq) + H_2(g)$$

24.4 Taking away hydrogen

Hydrogen and oxygen are chemically opposite in many ways. Adding oxygen gives the same result as taking away hydrogen. Chlorine is a poisonous gas but to counteract it on a small scale use a little ammonia, another poisonous gas. The chlorine takes away the hydrogen from the ammonia giving hydrogen chloride, yet another poisonous gas.

$$\text{ammonia} + \text{chlorine} \rightarrow \text{hydrogen chloride} + \text{nitrogen}$$
$$2NH_3(g) + 3Cl_2(g) \rightarrow 6HCl(g) \qquad\qquad + N_2(g)$$

The chlorine is the **oxidising agent** and the ammonia is the **reducing agent**. The hydrogen chloride then reacts with more ammonia to give ammonium chloride.

$$HCl(g) + NH_3(g) \rightarrow NH_4Cl(s)$$

The overall reaction is

$$8NH_3(g) + 3Cl_2(g) \rightarrow 6NH_4Cl(s) + N_2(g)$$

In a similar way, ammonia passing over hot copper oxide loses its hydrogen and so is oxidised to nitrogen. What will you see in this reaction?

$$3CuO(s) + 2NH_3(g) \rightarrow 3Cu(s) + 3H_2O(l) + N_2(g)$$

24.5 Increasing the proportion of a non-metal in a compound

The oxidation of iron can occur in two stages. Hydrochloric acid or gaseous hydrogen chloride will oxidise iron to iron(II) chloride.

iron	+	hydrochloric acid or hydrogen chloride	$\rightarrow$	iron(II) chloride	+	hydrogen
$Fe(s)$	+	$2HCl(aq)$	$\rightarrow$	$FeCl_2(aq)$	+	$H_2(g)$
$Fe(s)$	+	$2HCl(g)$	$\rightarrow$	$FeCl_2(s)$	+	$H_2(g)$

If chlorine gas is passed into iron(II) chloride solution then iron(III) chloride solution is formed.

$$2FeCl_2(aq) + Cl_2(g) \rightarrow 2FeCl_3(aq)$$

Iron(III) chloride can be produced in one stage by passing dry chlorine gas over hot iron, see Section 23.2.

$$2Fe(s) + 3Cl_2(g) \rightarrow 2FeCl_3(s)$$

So you can make iron(III) chloride in the two stages:

iron	$\rightarrow$	iron(II) chloride	$\rightarrow$	iron(III) chloride
Fe	$\rightarrow$	$FeCl_2$	$\rightarrow$	$FeCl_3$

or directly. For every atom of iron there are 0, 2 or 3 atoms of chlorine. The iron is being oxidised in two stages.

In a big fire you may have carbon being oxidised in two stages.

carbon	$\rightarrow$	carbon monoxide	$\rightarrow$	carbon dioxide
C		CO		CO_2

When you get energy by oxidising glucose in your muscles there are many stages in the reactions.

24.6 Oxidation and electrons

When magnesium is oxidised it loses electrons to the oxygen or chlorine. A magnesium atom has the electronic structure 2,8,2, see Chapter 28. In its compounds you have magnesium cations of electronic structure 2,8 (like neon). The oxygen atom has the electronic structure 2,6 and the oxide anion the electronic structure 2,8 (like neon). The electrons are transferred from the metal to the non-metal when you make the ionic compound, magnesium oxide.

24.7 Reduction and oxidation

Reduction is the opposite of oxidation. In a reaction, if something is oxidised, something else must be reduced. You can't have one reaction without the other: they are complementary. Together they are known as **redox reactions**. Whether you say a reaction is an oxidation or a reduction depends on your point of view or what you want to emphasise. You can define reduction as:

loss of oxygen
gain of hydrogen
increasing the proportion of a metal in a compound
adding electrons to an atom, molecule or ion,

just as in previous sections we have discussed oxidation as:

gain of oxygen
loss of hydrogen
increasing the proportion of a non-metal in a compound
losing electrons from an atom, molecule or ion.

A useful phrase to remember when ionic compounds are concerned in reduction–oxidation or redox reactions is OIL RIG:

Oxidation Is Loss, Reduction Is Gain (of electrons)

You can go back to the start of this chapter and look at all the reactions again with these thoughts in your mind. Here are three examples.

$$CH_4(g) + 2O_2(g) \rightarrow CO_2(g) + 2H_2O(l)$$

The oxygen gains hydrogen or carbon, so the oxygen is reduced.

$$Fe(s) + 2HCl(aq) \rightarrow FeCl_2(aq) + H_2(g)$$

The iron gains chlorine so it is oxidised; the hydrochloric acid loses hydrogen so the acid is reduced.

When you burn magnesium in oxygen the oxygen atoms gain electrons so they are reduced.

	magnesium	+ oxygen	→ magnesium oxide
Electronic structure of atom or ion	2,8,2	2,6	Mg^{2+} 2,8 O^{2-} 2,8

Thus an ion–electron equation for the oxidation of magnesium is

$$Mg \rightarrow Mg^{2+} + 2e^-$$

and for the reduction of oxygen

$$O + 2e^- \rightarrow O^{2-}$$

You must be careful to state whether you are talking about a substance (an agent) or its reaction (a process). Remember an oxidising agent is reduced in a reaction but a reducing agent is oxidised in a reaction. You can show this by arrows:

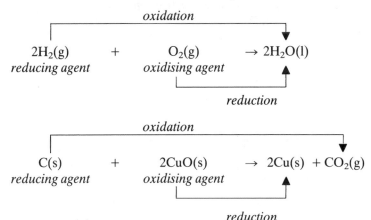

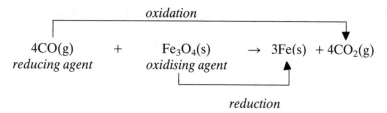

24.8 How to identify an oxidising agent

You add a reducing agent and look for a colour change. So to your unknown substance you may add:

(a) dilute sulphuric acid and *potassium iodide* solution and see if the colour changes from colourless to brown (iodine solution) or even black (solid iodine). Iodine can be confirmed by adding starch solution, which goes blue-black.

(b) dilute hydrochloric acid and *sodium sulphite* solution (or use sulphur dioxide gas) and see if a sulphate is formed. A sulphate is identified if a white precipitate is formed with barium chloride solution, in the presence of hydrochloric acid.

(c) *concentrated hydrochloric acid* and warm the mixture in a fume cupboard and see if chlorine is formed. Chlorine is a yellow-green gas which turns damp litmus paper from blue to red very quickly and then bleaches (decolorises) it.

(d) dilute sulphuric acid and *iron(II) sulphate* solution and see if an iron(III) compound is produced. An iron(III) compound will give a red-brown precipitate with plenty of sodium hydroxide or ammonia solution.

Not all these tests will work with a particular oxidising agent, so several should be tried.

24.9 How to identify a reducing agent

You add an oxidising agent and look for a colour change. So to your unknown substance you may add:

(a) dilute sulphuric acid and *potassium manganate(VII)* solution and see if the purple colour disappears (decolorised).

(*b*) dilute sulphuric acid and *potassium dichromate(VI)* solution and see if the colour changes from orange to green.

(*c*) *iodine* solution and see if the colour changes from brown to colourless.

(*d*) dilute hydrochloric acid and *iron(III) chloride* solution and see if an iron(II) compound is produced. An iron(II) compound will give a green precipitate with plenty of sodium hydroxide or ammonia solution.

(For two further tests used in organic chemistry, see Section 19.3.) Not all these tests will work with a particular reducing agent so several should be tried.

24.10 Oxidation is important

We move, grow and keep warm by oxidation of the food we eat, see Section 26.2. When we are not warm enough we oxidise (burn) fossil fuels such as methane, coal or petroleum or they are burnt in power stations to make electricity.

When we throw things away and they rot on the local authority dump or on a compost heap, then oxidation plays a large part in the reactions involved.

When we want metals to build bridges, buildings, cars, ships, planes and so on, then usually we start with a metal compound and reduce it to the metal. At the same time something else is oxidised. A major problem with any metal we use is that it will corrode and form a compound again: this is an oxidation.

Together with acid–base reactions (see Chapter 21), we are dependent upon redox reactions. The most powerful way of carrying out redox reactions is by electrolysis, see Chapter 14.

25

The Activity Series

25.1 The chemical properties of metals

The elements can be divided into metals and non-metals. The physical properties of metals were discussed in Sections 11.1 and 15.4. Chemical properties can also be used to classify elements as metals or non-metals, see Figure 25.1. There is a huge difference between burning magnesium in air and heating a piece of copper

Chemical properties	Metals	Non-metals
Type	reducing agents	oxidising agents
Ions formed	cations	anions
With non-metals	form ionic compounds	form covalent compounds
With metals	form alloys	form ionic compounds
With dilute acids	give a metal salt and hydrogen	no reaction
With alkalis	many do not react; a few are amphoteric (see Section 22.3)	many react, but in a complex way
With oxygen	form basic oxides	form acidic oxides
With chlorine	form salts which are stable to water	form compounds which are unstable to water (hydrolysis)
With hydrogen	a few react to give definite compounds	many react to give definite compounds

Fig. 25.1. The chemical properties of metals and non-metals

which only oxidises on the surface. So chemical properties can also be studied to put the metals in an order of activity.

25.2 How to obtain the activity series

The metals can be arranged in order with the most reactive at the top and the least reactive at the bottom. To compare them you must use pieces of metal of the same size. How fast or how vigorously does each metal react in a set of experiments? You can start by seeing if oxygen from the air reacts with the metal at room temperature, or if the metal needs heating before anything starts happening. In most cases, when heated:

$$\text{metal} + \text{oxygen} \rightarrow \text{metal oxide}$$

Secondly, you can put each metal in water or steam. Often:

$$\text{metal} + \text{water} \rightarrow \text{metal oxide (or hydroxide)} + \text{hydrogen}$$

At this stage you might decide it is wise not to do any further experiments with some metals because they are so reactive. A third set of experiments is to put the metals in dilute hydrochloric acid. In some cases:

$$\text{metal} + \text{acid} \rightarrow \text{metal salt} + \text{hydrogen}$$

A fourth set of experiments is about displacement or replacement reactions. When you put a metal such as zinc in a solution of copper sulphate the solution gets warm, the blue colour fades and a red-brown solid forms. The zinc has displaced the copper and formed colourless zinc sulphate solution:

Zinc	+ copper(II)	→ zinc sulphate	+ copper
(grey solid)	sulphate	*(colourless*	*(red-brown*
	(blue solution)	*solution)*	*solid)*
$Zn(s)$	+ $CuSO_4(aq)$	→ $ZnSO_4(aq)$ +	$Cu(s)$

In general, if metal 1 is more reactive than metal 2:

metal 1 + metal 2 in compound
$$\rightarrow \text{metal 1 in compound} + \text{metal 2}$$

From these four sets of experiments you can draw up the order of activity (reactivity). You should get the same or nearly the same order from each experiment, so it is reasonable to take an average. There is an electrical experiment (measuring voltages, see Section 6.1) which is another way of proving these results hence the alternative title, the electrochemical series. An outline of the results is given in Figure 25.2.

25.3 Further evidence

When you have arranged the metals in order of reactivity, you may notice that the elements at the bottom have been known a long time

Elements in order of decreasing activity	Reaction with oxygen (air)	Reaction with water
Potassium	corrodes quickly, on heating burns readily with lilac flame	dangerously reactive
Sodium	corrodes quickly, on heating burns readily with orange-yellow flame	very reactive
Calcium	tarnishes slowly, on heating burns suddenly with red flame	quite reactive
Magnesium	tarnishes slowly, on heating burns brightly with white flame	reacts slowly with hot water, burns in steam
Aluminium	tarnishes slowly, on heating powder burns readily	surface reaction
Zinc	tarnishes slowly, on heating powder burns readily; zinc oxide is yellow if hot	surface reaction
Iron	tarnishes slowly, on heating filings burn with sparks; the oxide formed is black	reacts when heated in steam, the oxide formed is black
Lead	tarnishes very slowly, on heating oxidises slowly; the oxide formed is yellow or red	none
Copper	tarnishes very slowly, on heating surface formation only of oxide (black)	none

Fig. 25.2.   The activity or electrochemical series

and the elements at the top are 'modern' metals. The elements at the top are too reactive to occur naturally as elements. Another way of saying this is that the compounds of the metals at the top are the most difficult to decompose. Therefore the order of activity of the elements is the order of stability of their compounds: the most reactive elements which have the most stable compounds at the top; the least reactive elements which have the least stable compounds at the bottom.

Two common reducing agents are hydrogen and carbon. Hydrogen can be used to change the oxides to the metals. Carbon is able to change more oxides to metals. However several metals form

Reaction with dilute hydrochloric acid	*Displacement reactions with compounds of metals below element in activity series*
very reactive	reacts with water
very reactive	as potassium
quite reactive	as potassium
quite reactive	fast
quite reactive	only fast if surface is clean
quite reactive	fast
fairly reactive, iron(II) chloride solution formed (pale green)	moderate
none (but will react slowly with dilute nitric acid)	very slow
as lead	none

compounds with carbon and so the metal itself is not produced. So the most reactive metals are not obtained by heating their oxides with carbon.

Compounds of the elements in order of decreasing stability	Reaction of hydrogen with metal oxide	Reaction of carbon with metal oxide
Potassium Sodium	none	none
Calcium Magnesium	none	calcium forms a carbide
Aluminium	none	forms a carbide
Zinc	none	gives metal + carbon dioxide
Iron(II) Iron(III)	gives metal + steam	as zinc
Lead(II)	as iron	as zinc
Copper(II)	as iron	as zinc

Fig. 25.3. The stability of metal compounds

More evidence for the activity series can be obtained by studying the action of heat on metal nitrates, metal carbonates and metal hydroxides. An outline of the results is given in Figure 25.3.

Reaction when metal nitrate is heated	*Reaction when metal carbonate is heated*	*Reaction when metal hydroxide is heated*
give metal nitrite + oxygen	none	none
give metal oxide + nitrogen dioxide + oxygen	give metal oxide + carbon dioxide	give metal oxide + steam
as calcium	carbonate does not exist	as calcium
as calcium	as calcium	as calcium
iron(II) nitrate does not exist; iron(III) nitrate gives iron(III) oxide (red), nitrogen dioxide + oxygen	iron(II) carbonate gives iron(II) diiron(III) oxide (black) + carbon dioxide; iron(III) carbonate unknown	as calcium
gives lead(II) oxide (yellow or red) + nitrogen dioxide + oxygen	gives lead(II) oxide (yellow or red) + carbon dioxide	gives lead(II) oxide (yellow or red) + steam
gives copper(II) oxide (black) + nitrogen dioxide + oxygen	gives copper(II) oxide (black) + carbon dioxide	gives copper(II) oxide (black) + steam

26

Energy Changes

26.1 Changes and temperatures

If you fill a beaker of water from the tap you will find that its temperature is about 15 °C. It may be more in the summer or less in the winter. If you put the water in the icebox of the fridge and look at it every few minutes you will find its temperature drops and then stays the same, see Figure 26.1. The temperature remains constant while the water freezes and then it may drop further. When a liquid becomes a solid, heat is given out but the temperature remains constant. You may also notice that the ice pushes its way up in the beaker as the water freezes. The density of ice is less than that of water. This is one of the many strange properties of water.

If you take the beaker of ice out of the fridge, the warmth of the room will reverse the changes measured above. Heat is needed to

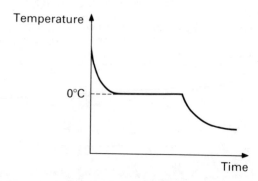

Fig. 26.1. A temperature-time graph for some water cooling

change a solid into a liquid and while this change is happening the temperature remains constant.

When heat is given out in a change, the change is **exothermic**. When heat is taken in in a change, the change is **endothermic**.

Natural gas is a **fuel** and when it burns it gives out heat. This is an exothermic chemical reaction. In words we write:

methane + oxygen → carbon dioxide + steam + heat

but in symbols we must write:

$$CH_4(g) + 2O_2(g) \rightarrow CO_2(g) + 2H_2O(l); \qquad \Delta H = -890 \text{ kJ/mol}$$

When methane (1 mole, 16 g, or 24 l) is burnt at constant atmospheric pressure and all the substances are in their usual states (at a standard 25 °C) then 890 kilojoules of heat are given out. The symbol for the energy change is ΔH; the value is given a negative sign because energy is given out by the change.

You can continue the experiment with the beaker of water by heating it. This gives you the graph shown in Figure 26.2. Up to 100 °C some water may change into a gas – it evaporates. At 100 °C bubbles of steam form in many places in the water and all of it slowly changes into steam – it boils. The temperature does not change while the water is boiling.

Why does the temperature remain constant during freezing or melting and during boiling or condensation? In ice, the water molecules are in fixed positions. When you heat it, the heat energy is used to overcome the forces holding the molecules together. When

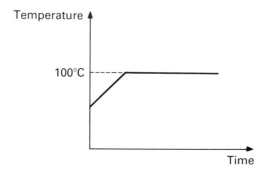

Fig. 26.2. A temperature-time graph for some water being heated

all the ice has melted, the heat energy increases the temperature of the water. In liquid water the molecules are moving at random but are nearly always touching one another. At the boiling point, the heat energy is used to make the molecules move much further apart as in a gas. The temperature remains constant until all the water has turned to steam. Then the heat energy increases the temperature of the steam.

Water is an odd liquid – it needs a lot of energy to melt ice or boil water, because its molecules are held together by hydrogen bonding (see Section 2.5) which is stronger than van der Waals forces, see Section 31.4.

26.2 Exothermic chemical changes

The combustion of natural gas is described above. Road menders and caravanners use propane (C_3H_8) and butane (C_4H_{10}) as bottled gases. Both these hydrocarbons are good fuels. In your car you use octane (C_8H_{18}) mixed with many similar substances. For a barbecue you use charcoal, which is almost pure carbon. The complete combustion of carbon gives carbon dioxide, and the equation is

$$C(s) + O_2(g) \rightarrow CO_2(g); \qquad \Delta H = -394 \text{ kJ/mol}$$

When you have eaten food your body breaks down the molecules into smaller ones. Carbohydrates (starch and sugars) are broken down into glucose ($C_6H_{12}O_6$). Glucose is called a biological fuel. It is used by plants as well as by us. In respiration, glucose reacts with the oxygen carried by the red cells (haemoglobin) of your blood. Gradually glucose changes to carbon dioxide and water, releasing a lot of energy. Athletes and climbers sometimes suck glucose tablets for a quick source of energy.

$$C_6H_{12}O_6(s) + 6O_2(g) \rightarrow 6CO_2(g) + 6H_2O(l);$$
$$\Delta H = -2815 \text{ kJ/mol}$$

The carbon dioxide is carried away by your blood. The energy keeps you warm and helps your muscles work.

If you drip water on to anhydrous copper(II) sulphate you will see the colour change from white to blue. At the same time heat is given out. The reverse change, dehydration of the hydrated salt, absorbs heat. When concentrated sulphuric acid is poured carefully into water a lot of heat is given out. The covalent acid reacts with water, producing many hydrogen, hydrogensulphate and sulphate ions.

The neutralisation of an acid by a base is another exothermic reaction. When a strong alkali neutralises a strong acid and produces water, the heat released is always 57 kJ/mol.

26.3 Activation energy

Exothermic reactions do not always occur spontaneously. Energy is given out by the reaction but some energy may be needed to get the reaction started. You have to *activate* molecules before the atoms move into new patterns. The activation energy may be supplied by friction, by an electrical spark, by heating or by using a catalyst. More heat is given out when the reaction occurs than is taken in to start the reaction, see Figure 26.3.

A good example is the synthesis of iron(II) sulphide. You have to heat the elements to start the reaction but, once started, the reaction continues on its own. The elements glow because more heat is given out by the reaction than is taken in to start it.

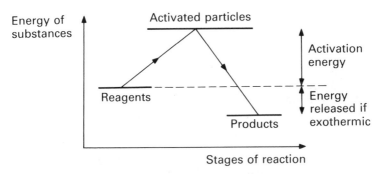

Fig. 26.3. Activation energy

Another way of describing many reactions is by the triangle of fire, see Figure 26.4. To cause a fire you need three things. You can put out a fire by the three opposite things: cooling the materials, switching off the fuel supply or preventing oxygen (air) getting to the fire. Think about the ways you would put out fires of burning paper, fat in a chip pan, and burning gas on a stove.

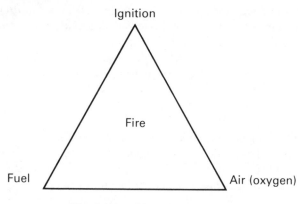

Fig. 26.4. The triangle of fire

The flash point of a substance is the temperature at which the gas above the substance will catch fire and burn for a moment.

Flash points can be found in various ways. A danger sign is put on containers of liquids which have a flash point below 21 °C. The flash points of some common liquids are:

	Flash point (°C)
ethanoic acid (pure acetic acid)	+43
ethanol (alcohol)	+13
2,2,4-trimethylpentane (the octane in petrol)	−10
propanone (acetone, nail varnish remover)	−18

The ignition temperature of a substance is the temperature at which the substance will catch fire and keep burning in air.

The ignition temperature of petrol is 550 °C and of hydrogen 580 °C. Natural fibres have a low flammability – wool fails to burn more than 1000 metres above sea level because of lack of oxygen. Synthetic fibres, such as nylon and Terylene, have ignition temperatures above their melting points. If you are caught in a fire wearing nylon clothing, the nylon melts at 263 °C and then it sticks to your skin, conducting heat to you. For an oil the ignition temperature may be called the fire point.

26.4 Endothermic changes

We all depend on the most important endothermic change in the world: photosynthesis, see Sections 7.1 and 24.2. The energy of sunlight falls on green plants which contain chlorophyll. The plants grow by making sugars and starches, giving out oxygen into the air. Thus the plants provide us with food and with the oxygen we need for respiration and for burning fuels.

When a solid dissolves in water there is often a drop in temperature. Dissolving is equivalent to melting and mixing. Melting is always an endothermic change. This experiment can be tried with ammonium chloride or potassium nitrate.

Thermal decompositions of compounds are endothermic reactions. The thermal decomposition of copper(II) carbonate is easy; that of calcium carbonate is difficult. Studying these changes is one way of putting the metals in the order known as the activity series, see Figure 25.2. The cracking of large molecules in crude oil into small molecules is an important step in making many other substances, see Sections 25.3 and 19.3.

Photography depends on the endothermic reaction:

$$\text{silver bromide} \rightarrow \text{silver} + \text{bromine}$$

The energy for the reaction is supplied by light falling on the film. When the film is developed, the reverse of the picture appears. From this 'negative' a 'positive' print is made. By including light-sensitive dyes in the film, we can get colour photographs.

27

Rates of Changes

27.1 Slow and fast reactions

How quickly can you digest a meal? That's rather hard to measure
and it varies from person to person. Fats take longer to digest than
carbohydrates.

How quickly does iron rust? It depends on the conditions (see
Section 7.9) but it is easier to measure than the rate of digestion – by
weighing the iron as it forms hydrated iron(III) oxide.

How quickly does a base neutralise an acid? If you have indigestion from too much hydrochloric acid in your stomach then some
medicines may act quicker than others. When an alkali neutralises
an acid in a test tube or a conical flask the reaction is so fast you
cannot measure its rate. How quickly does a precipitate of barium
sulphate form in a test for a sulphate, or of silver chloride in a test for
a chloride? Again these reactions are much too fast for you to
measure.

In between the extremes of slow and fast there are many reactions
which you can study in the laboratory. There are many ways of
studying the rates of reactions. You can weigh substances as a gas
escapes or as a gas reacts with a solid or a liquid. You can measure
volumes of gases used or produced. You may watch for the appearance or disappearance of a coloured substance. In these experiments you can study the importance of

(*a*) the surface area of a solid, concentration of a solution or
    pressure of a gas,
(*b*) the temperature, and
(*c*) the presence or absence of a catalyst.

27.2 The surface area of solids

If you have some large crystals of copper(II) sulphate and stir them into water, they dissolve quite slowly. If you crush the crystals, the same mass will dissolve more quickly. A finely divided solid has a bigger surface area and reacts faster.

If you take some large lumps of calcium carbonate and put them into hydrochloric acid there are two ways you can study the reaction. You can measure the total mass in an open vessel. This decreases as the carbon dioxide produced escapes into the surrounding air. An alternative is to measure the volume of the carbon dioxide as it forms. In both experiments you can plot a graph of the results, see Figure 27.1. The two graphs have the same basic shape, after allowing for differences of scale; although of course the mass *decreases* and the volume of carbon dioxide *increases* with time. The slope or gradient of the graph tells you how fast the reaction is going. It is fast at the start and gets slower as time goes by. At the end of the graph the line is horizontal because nothing is changing.

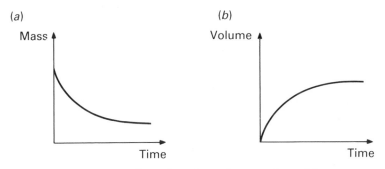

Fig. 27.1. Reaction of a carbonate plus acid

You can repeat the experiment with small lumps of calcium carbonate and a new portion of acid. The reaction is quicker to get to the end this time.

Industry knows the dangers of powders being much more reactive than large lumps of solids. In coal mines they do their best to lay the dust. A custard powder factory and an aluminium powder factory have had serious explosions caused by fine particles.

27.3 The concentrations of solutions

If you use the same size of lumps of calcium carbonate you can study the effect of concentration of the acid. You must use the same mass of calcium carbonate each time and the same volume of hydrochloric acid. You will find that the rate increases as the concentration of the acid increases. A similar experiment is to time the reaction of pieces of magnesium ribbon in nitric acid of different concentrations. The ribbon soon dissolves and disappears.

Another experiment that is easy to do is to add an acid to sodium thiosulphate ($Na_2S_2O_3$) solution. A precipitate of sulphur forms. You can time how long it takes for a mark under the beaker to disappear from view as the precipitate makes the solution go cloudy.

The results of these experiments can be drawn as graphs, see Figure 27.2. In graph (a) the time of reaction is plotted against the concentration of the substance that is being studied. The reciprocal of the time (1/time) is a way of describing the rate of the reaction. Graph (b) may be a straight line (i) or a curve (ii) because the rate does not always depend directly on concentration.

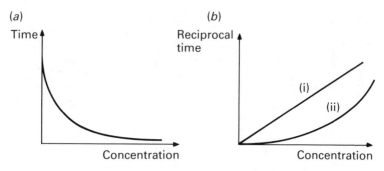

Fig. 27.2. The influence of concentration upon time of reaction

27.4 The pressures of gases

Many important industrial reactions use gases. The pressure of a gas is a way of expressing its concentration. Increasing the pressure of the gases in a reaction increases the rate of reaction. So the synthesis of ammonia from nitrogen and hydrogen in the Haber process is usually done at high pressures, see Section 18.3. The synthesis of poly(ethene) is usually done at very high pressures. At 1500 times normal pressure, low density 'polythene' is made on a large scale, see Section 20.1. When margarine and cooking fat are made from natural oils the pressure is often about five times normal pressure, see Section 17.9.

The contact process for making sulphur trioxide is usually done at normal pressure because the substances are diluted with nitrogen from the air, see Section 18.2. It is not worth expending energy to compress all that nitrogen, which will only be released back into the atmosphere.

27.5 The influence of temperature

In spring the grass starts growing again. When the average temperature goes up by 10 °C then the rate of growth is doubled. People are chemical reactions on two legs. Our body temperature is about 37 °C. If your temperature goes down then the chemical reactions necessary to keep you alive occur too slowly. If your temperature goes up too much then reactions occur too fast for your comfort.

You can study many simple reactions in the laboratory to see how the temperature influences them, for example an acid with sodium thiosulphate or with magnesium ribbon. A more colourful example is the redox reaction of potassium manganate(VII) with ethanedioic acid in the presence of dilute sulphuric acid. You can time the disappearance of the purple colour from mixtures at 50 °C, 60 °C, 70 °C, 80 °C and so on.

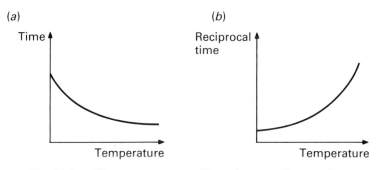

Fig. 27.3.   How temperature affects the rate of a reaction

For all these experiments you can plot a graph of time against temperature. As before you could also plot a graph of reciprocal time (a better measure of the rate) against temperature, see Figure 27.3.

In industry there are many reactions that are speeded up by increasing the temperature – sometimes by several hundred degrees and occasionally by two or three thousand degrees Celsius. Putting up the temperature gives more and more molecules the activation energy they need for a reaction to occur, see Section 26.3. It also increases the rate of collision of the particles of substances. Some typical industrial processes that are done at high temperatures are listed in Figure 27.4.

Process	Temperature ($^{\circ}C$)	Section of book
Hardening oils	180	17·9
Sulphur trioxide	420	18·2
Ammonia	450	18·3
Cracking oil	550	5·3
Limekiln	1150	16·4
Steel	1650	15·3
Blast furnace (iron)	1900	15·2

Fig. 27.4. Industrial processes carried out at high temperatures

If hydrogen is to be used for nuclear fusion to provide energy in the same way that the sun gives out energy, the temperature must be over ten million degrees Celsius. Will we ever be able to obtain it in a controlled way, see Section 6.4?

27.6 Catalysts

If you have some hydrogen peroxide and look carefully at it you may notice a few bubbles of oxygen slowly escaping. If you raise the temperature the reaction occurs a bit faster but it is still hard to prove that oxygen escapes. However, there is a rapid reaction if you add a drop of blood, even at room temperature. In blood there are enzymes – naturally occurring substances that speed up the reactions of other substances. Our bodies contain enzymes in every cell, each enzyme has its own purpose. Some of the enzymes in our blood stop us being poisoned by the build-up of hydrogen peroxide as an unwanted substance.

In the laboratory you may prefer to use manganese(IV) oxide as the catalyst for decomposing hydrogen peroxide. You can weigh the powder before and after the experiment. It is unchanged in mass as well as appearance and chemical properties. You can use the powder time and time again – it is not consumed in the reaction.

The decomposition of hydrogen peroxide can be studied with various quantities of catalyst, at different temperatures or with different concentrations of solution. You can plot a graph of the results as in Figure 27.1(b).

A catalyst does its job by altering the way in which a reaction occurs. The new reaction 'pathway' has a lower activation energy and so more molecules have the necessary energy to react at lower temperatures. Catalysts are sometimes so effective that they seem to start reactions which otherwise are very, very slow. For example, you can store hydrogen and oxygen together for years and nothing seems to happen. If you add some platinum the gases rapidly combine to form water. (A spark would also cause the reaction but a spark is not a catalyst because it cannot be regained.)

Process	Catalyst	Section of book
Hardening oils	nickel	17·9
Sulphur trioxide	vanadium(V) oxide	18·2
Ammonia	iron	18·3
Cracking oil	aluminium oxide	5·3
Nitric acid	platinum	18·4

Fig. 27.5. Some industrial processes that use a catalyst

27.7 Reversible reactions

Copper(II) sulphate-5-water can be dehydrated by heating the blue crystals. The white anhydrous solid produced can be hydrated by adding water. The reaction is reversible. When the reaction is reversible by altering the conditions, two full arrows are drawn in equations:

copper(II) sulphate-5-water $\rightleftarrows$ copper(II) sulphate + water

Fig. 27.6. Platinum gauze catalyst being placed in an ammonia burner for the manufacture of nitric acid

There are many chemical reactions which are reversible. If you heat the reagents in a closed container they react to form the products. After a while the so-called products have accumulated to such an extent that the reverse reaction becomes important. The rates of the forward and backward reactions eventually become equal. It is a case of dynamic (or kinetic) **equilibrium**. The reaction has not stopped but the proportions of reagents and products remain constant. This is shown in equations by double half-arrows. If calcium carbonate is heated in a *closed* container, then the reaction is reversible.

calcium carbonate $\rightleftharpoons$ calcium oxide + carbon dioxide

In a limekiln this does *not* apply because the carbon dioxide is pushed out by the nitrogen of the air. The reverse reaction cannot occur.

There are many important industrial reactions which are reversible. In the synthesis of ammonia the conditions chosen have to be a compromise between having a high rate (by a high temperature) and having a high yield (by a low temperature). Fortunately, the increased pressure increases the rate *and* the yield. In the manufacture of sulphur trioxide the same restrictions apply, although the pressure used is nearer to normal. Catalysts are important in both of these processes because they cause a high rate of reaction even though the temperature is fairly low.

28

The Structure of Atoms

28.1 The modern atomic theory

Dalton's atomic theory (see Section 10.4), helped to explain many experiments. With tables of the masses of atoms you can calculate the masses of substances in reactions. However, as scientists did more experiments they found problems that Dalton's theory could not answer, such as:

(a) Why do elements have different valencies (combining powers) and why are these valencies whole numbers?
(b) Why do molecules of compounds have a definite shape?
(c) Why are there definite patterns of particles in crystals?
(d) Why do only metals and some compounds conduct electricity?
(e) What is radioactivity? (Atoms of one element which are radioactive change into atoms of another element.)
(f) How can isotopes exist? (Isotopes are atoms of one element which have different masses.)
(g) How can large numbers of atoms combine to give the huge molecules of plastics, fibres and many biological compounds?

To explain these facts we need a theory that describes the structure of an atom.

28.2 The atom is split into three

The modern atomic theory is based on the results of passing electricity through gases. By the early 1900s two particles smaller than atoms had been discovered. One was the electron, which has a negative charge; the other was the proton, which has a positive charge. In an atom there are equal numbers of electrons and protons. An atom is neutral.

If an atom loses an electron it becomes an **ion**, a particle with a positive charge. This positive particle is called a **cation**, for example H^+ is a hydrogen ion. If an atom gains an electron it also becomes an ion, this time with a negative charge. This negative particle is called an **anion**, for example Cl^- is a chloride ion. Voltaic and electrolytic cells depend on the presence of ions, see Chapters 6 and 14.

Ions are charged particles. Electrons and cations carry electricity through gases. Many solids are made up of ions rather than atoms or molecules. When these solids are melted or dissolved in water the ions can move. These molten solids and aqueous solutions are electrolytes: they are conductors of electricity and chemical reactions occur when the ions reach the electrodes.

The third particle which is found in nearly every atom is a neutron. It is the most difficult to find because it has no charge. Neutrons and protons have almost the same mass – we call it 1. An electron has a much smaller mass, about 1/1840th of a proton's mass: this is so small that we ignore it for most experiments. To emphasise that an electron and a proton have equal and opposite electrical charges we call the charges -1 and $+1$. These masses and charges are all ratios and so have no units, see Figure 28.1.

Particle	Symbol	Mass	Charge
Electron	e^-	1/1840	-1
Proton	p	1	$+1$
Neutron	n	1	0

Fig. 28.1. The relative masses and charges of three sub-atomic particles

28.3 A typical atom

The centre or nucleus of a typical atom is made up of protons and neutrons. This is true for every atom except one kind of hydrogen atom. The mass of the nucleus is approximately equal to the mass of the atom. The number of neutrons and protons gives the **mass**

number of an atom. The number of protons gives the **atomic number**. To describe one particular atom, sometimes called a nuclide, you can write the name as, for example, carbon-12 or as the symbol ^{12}C. This means the carbon atom of mass number 12. Carbon has an atomic number of 6; it has six protons in the nucleus of each atom so a more detailed symbol for this atom is $^{12}_{6}C$. This atom contains 6 protons and 6 neutrons in its nucleus, making up a total of 12 particles, see Figure 28.2.

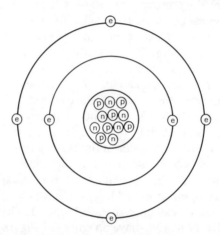

Fig. 28.2. A typical atom of carbon. The central nucleus consists of 6 protons (mass 6, charge +6) and 6 neutrons (mass 6, charge 0). The atomic number is 6 (number of protons). The mass number is 12 (number of neutrons and protons). There are 6 electrons (charge −6) to balance the nuclear charge. The electrons are arranged around the nucleus in shells: 2 then 4

There is a less common variety of carbon atom. It has 7 neutrons in its nucleus. It still has 6 protons, otherwise it would not be carbon. Ordinary carbon is a mixture of these two kinds of atoms, called isotopes. (Isotopes are nuclides belonging to the same element.)

Isotopes are kinds of atoms of the same element which have the same numbers of protons but different numbers of neutrons. They have different masses.

Ordinary carbon consists of about 99% ^{12}C and about 1% ^{13}C atoms. The average mass of an atom of carbon is 12·01. This average (called a weighted mean) is the **relative atomic mass** of carbon. For most purposes you can take it as 12 because you cannot do experiments accurately enough to make it worthwhile being so precise.

There is a third variety of carbon atom, ^{14}C, see Figure 28.3. This one is radioactive: all the time it is changing into nitrogen. It is formed in the upper atmosphere and all living matter (people, animals, plants) contains a tiny percentage of it in compounds. When you die and when plants die the percentage goes down as the ^{14}C changes to nitrogen. This gives us a way of finding the length of time since a plant or an animal died. It is called carbon dating and can be used to date objects up to 50 000 years old, see also Section 28.5.

The nucleus in a typical atom is surrounded by electrons. The electrons are arranged in shells. The shells are drawn as circles in

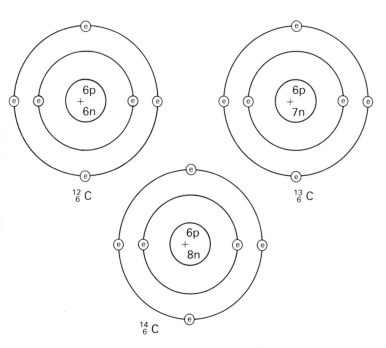

Fig. 28.3. The isotopes of carbon

diagrams. You can think of the electrons as being like satellites going round the earth. Another way of thinking about them is to imagine the nucleus as a screwed-up ball of paper put in one envelope and this then put in a second and a third envelope and so on. Each envelope represents a shell of electrons. The electrons have different energies. The electrons close to the nucleus, in the first shell, are strongly attracted by the nucleus. There are one or two electrons in the first shell. The second shell is further away. Its electrons are not attracted so strongly but eight electrons can fit in it. The third shell can only contain eight electrons for the first 20 elements in the periodic table.

28.4 Electronic structures

The electronic structure of the atom of an element is the key to many of its properties. It helps you to decide whether an element is a metal or a non-metal and whether it is a reducing agent or an oxidising agent. It helps you to explain the valency or combining power of an element. It also tells you whether a compound is likely to be of one type or another, see Chapters 29 and 30. The periodic table of the elements is based upon electronic structures.

The atomic number of an element tells you which element it is. Atomic number is defined as the number of protons but it also tells you the number of electrons in an atom because an atom is neutral. The shells of electrons are filled going outwards from the nucleus, see Figure 28.4.

Elements with only a few electrons in the outer shell are metallic in their properties. They lose electrons in reactions and form cations. They are reducing agents. Their compounds with non-metals are ionic. The valency of a metal is the number of electrons it loses when it forms an ion.

Elements with many electrons in the outer shell are non-metallic in their properties. They either gain electrons in reactions with metals, thus forming anions, or they react with other non-metals by sharing electrons. The compounds of non-metals with one another are covalent. The valency of a non-metal is the number of electrons it gains when it forms an ion or shares in a covalent compound. Non-metals are oxidising agents.

The electrical conductance of a metal wire is due to the movement

Element	Symbol	Atomic number	Electronic structure
Hydrogen	H	1	1
Helium	He	2	2
Lithium	Li	3	2,1
Beryllium	Be	4	2,2
Boron	B	5	2,3
Carbon	C	6	2,4
Nitrogen	N	7	2,5
Oxygen	O	8	2,6
Fluorine	F	9	2,7
Neon	Ne	10	2,8
Sodium	Na	11	2,8,1
Magnesium	Mg	12	2,8,2
Aluminium	Al	13	2,8,3
Silicon	Si	14	2,8,4
Phosphorus	P	15	2,8,5
Sulphur	S	16	2,8,6
Chlorine	Cl	17	2,8,7
Argon	Ar	18	2,8,8
Potassium	K	19	2,8,8,1
Calcium	Ca	20	2,8,8,2

Fig. 28.4. The electronic structures of the first 20 elements

of the outer electrons of each atom which are shared by *all* the atoms in the crystal. Non-metals are non-conductors because the outer electrons of each atom are shared *only* with the next atom in a molecule – the molecules are then packed together to make the crystal of the solid. A lot of chemical facts can be explained by considering the behaviour of electrons.

28.5 Radioactivity

Sometimes the nucleus of an atom is not stable: it is radioactive. In a simple radioactive change the nucleus may emit one or more of these types of radiation:

an α (alpha) particle which is a helium nucleus, $^{4}_{2}He^{2+}$

a β (beta) particle which is an electron, e^{-}

a γ (gamma) ray which has a shorter wavelength than an X-ray

When α and β particles are lost by radioactive atoms one element changes into another. Sometimes one step gives a stable atom, for example radioactive sodium-24 changes into magnesium-24 by loss of a β particle. This electron is thought to be formed in the nucleus of the atom by a neutron changing into a proton plus an electron.

$$^{24}_{11}\text{Na} \rightarrow {}^{24}_{12}\text{Mg} + \text{e}^-$$

In other cases many steps occur before a stable atom is formed. For example, radioactive uranium-238 loses many α and β particles before it becomes a stable atom of lead-206.

$$^{238}_{92}\text{U} \rightarrow {}^{206}_{82}\text{Pb} + 8{}^{4}_{2}\text{He} + 6\text{e}^-$$

Energy is released at every stage. Radioactivity can be used to follow the path of elements in physical and chemical reactions, to start and stop chemical reactions, to find the age of a material (see Section 28.3) and to measure the thickness of a substance.

There is no way of starting or stopping radioactivity. There are radioactive substances in our bodies, in the rocks around us, in the air we breathe and in the water we drink. There are three factors to consider about radioactive substances.

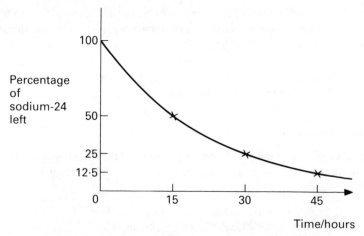

Fig. 28.5.   The decay of radioactive sodium-24

(*a*) The energy of the radiation. γ-rays are much more penetrating than α and β particles. The γ-radiation from cobalt-60 is used to treat cancer by stopping the wild growth of cells.

(*b*) The amount of the radioactive element present. In our bodies and in the sea the proportions of radioactive potassium-40 and hydrogen-3 are so small that we do not worry about them.

(*c*) The half-life of the radioactive element. The rate of decay (disappearance) of a radioactive element depends on the mass present, and so it is fast at the start and slow towards the end. It is measured by the **half-life** of the element, which is the time it takes for half the radioactive element to decay. Half-lives vary from seconds to billions of years. The graph in Figure 28.5 shows the decay of sodium-24 which has a half-life of 15 hours.

29

The Periodic Table

29.1 Early attempts at classifying elements

Antoine Lavoisier (1743–94, France) tried to divide the few elements he knew into classes. He had four classes:

(a) Metals, such as iron, copper, silver, gold and lead.
(b) Substances which he thought were metal oxides, such as aluminium oxide. He could not make aluminium from it.
(c) Non-metallic gases, such as hydrogen, nitrogen and oxygen.
(d) Non-metallic solids, such as carbon and sulphur.

Dalton suggested that the mass of an atom was its most important property, see Section 10.4. Johann Döbereiner (1780–1849, Germany) saw that similar elements often had relative atomic masses which were related:

lithium	7		chlorine	35·5	
sodium	23	16 between each	bromine	80	approximately 45 between each
potassium	39		iodine	127	

By the time of John Newlands (1837–98, England), scientists knew about 60 elements. Newlands put them in order of relative atomic mass and noticed that the eighth one was like the first, the ninth like the second . . . rather like octaves of notes in music:

> lithium 3, sodium 11, potassium 19 . . .
> boron 5, aluminium 13 . . .
> oxygen 8, sulphur 16 . . .

The numerical relationships were not always exact and in Newlands' time there were many elements yet to be discovered. Some people made fun of him but he was correct in thinking that the properties of elements did depend on numerical relationships.

29.2 Dmitri Mendeléev (1834–1907, USSR)

Mendeléev realised that missing elements could upset attempts at classification. He studied the physical and chemical properties of elements very carefully and then wrote a list of the elements, leaving gaps so that similar elements were in the same class or group. So group I included lithium, sodium and potassium, and group VII included chlorine, bromine and iodine.

The properties of the elements help us to put them in groups. The behaviour of members in a group is similar or even the same. One similarity of lithium and sodium is that they are both very reactive metals. Lithium and sodium form compounds of the same type of formula because they both have a valency of one, for example $LiCl$ and $NaCl$, and Li_2SO_4 and Na_2SO_4. Mendeléev called the repeating pattern of behaviour the periodic law (1869) and so the list of the elements was called the periodic table.

Mendeléev went one step further: he forecast the properties of some of the missing elements. He was amazingly successful. When gallium (1875), scandium (1879) and germanium (1886) were discovered, Mendeléev's table was regarded as a triumph because their properties are just what he had forecast.

In 1894 the first of the noble gases was discovered. This was argon and it did not fit into the periodic table. It was suggested that argon must be in a new group. If argon was the first member, where were the rest? It was not long before helium, neon, krypton, xenon and radon were discovered. They are usually called group 0 because for many years it was thought they had no chemical properties, see Section 17.10.

The discovery of argon also caused a second problem. The relative atomic masses of argon (39·95) and potassium (39·10) meant that if the order of mass was kept strictly, then argon should be put in group 1 with lithium and sodium, and potassium in group 0 as a noble gas. This is nonsense in terms of chemical properties. Soon it was realised that the atomic *number* of an element is more important than its relative atomic mass.

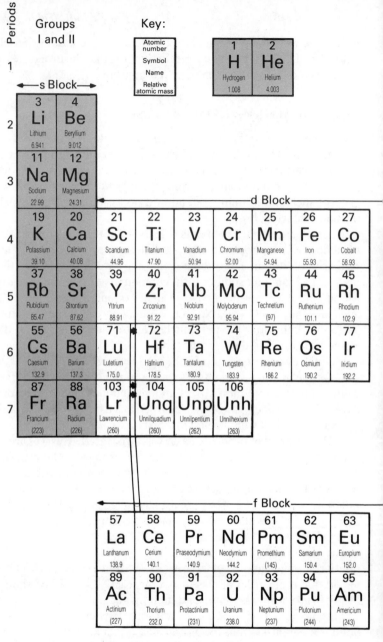

Fig. 29.1. The periodic table

THE PERIODIC TABLE

Groups

	III	IV	V	VI	VII	O
			◄────── p Block ──────►			
	5 **B** Boron 10.81	6 **C** Carbon 12.01	7 **N** Nitrogen 14.01	8 **O** Oxygen 16.00	9 **F** Fluorine 19.00	10 **Ne** Neon 20.18
	13 **Al** Aluminium 26.98	14 **Si** Silicon 28.09	15 **P** Phosphorus 30.97	16 **S** Sulphur 32.06	17 **Cl** Chlorine 35.45	18 **Ar** Argon 39.95

28 **Ni** Nickel 58.70	29 **Cu** Copper 63.55	30 **Zn** Zinc 65.38	31 **Ga** Gallium 69.72	32 **Ge** Germanium 72.59	33 **As** Arsenic 74.92	34 **Se** Selenium 78.96	35 **Br** Bromine 79.90	36 **Kr** Krypton 83.80
46 **Pd** Palladium 106.4	47 **Ag** Silver 107.9	48 **Cd** Cadmium 112.4	49 **In** Indium 114.8	50 **Sn** Tin 118.7	51 **Sb** Antimony 121.8	52 **Te** Tellurium 127.6	53 **I** Iodine 126.9	54 **Xe** Xenon 131.3
78 **Pt** Platinum 195.1	79 **Au** Gold 197.0	80 **Hg** Mercury 200.6	81 **Tl** Thallium 204.4	82 **Pb** Lead 207.2	83 **Bi** Bismuth 209.0	84 **Po** Polonium (209)	85 **At** Astatine (210)	86 **Rn** Radon (222)

| 64 **Gd** Gadolinium 157.3 | 65 **Tb** Terbium 158.9 | 66 **Dy** Dysprosium 162.5 | 67 **Ho** Holmium 164.9 | 68 **Er** Erbium 167.3 | 69 **Tm** Thulium 168.9 | 70 **Yb** Ytterbium 173.0 |
| 96 **Cm** Curium (247) | 97 **Bk** Berkelium (247) | 98 **Cf** Californium (251) | 99 **Es** Einsteinium (254) | 100 **Fm** Fermium (257) | 101 **Md** Mendelevium (258) | 102 **No** Nobelium (259) |

29.3 Atomic structure and the periodic table

The atoms of elements are made up of electrons, protons and neutrons, see Chapter 28. Henry Moseley (1887–1915, England) found that X-rays were given off by elements which were bombarded with electrons. The X-rays had a frequency that depended on the number of the element in the order given by the periodic table. This was true from 13 (aluminium) to 79 (gold). These are the atomic numbers of the elements. They describe the correct order of the elements in the periodic table, keeping argon and potassium each with their related elements.

Using atomic structure as a basis, there are four rules for drawing up the periodic table.

(*a*) The elements are put in order of atomic number. The atomic number is the number of protons in the nucleus of the atom of an element. An atom is neutral so it is also the number of electrons.

(*b*) Each time a new outer shell of electrons is started, a new line is started on the periodic table. These lines are called **periods**.

(*c*) The elements are put into columns, called **groups**. The elements in a group have the same number of electrons in the outer shell of their atoms.

(*d*) A rule for some of the elements beyond calcium, atomic number 20, which are called the **transition elements**: the elements are put into columns in which each element has the same number of electrons in the *penultimate* shell – the shell next to the outer shell.

When you understand these rules you can use the table to write down the electronic structures of the elements up to calcium. Hydrogen has one electron in the first shell. Helium has two electrons in the first shell. Lithium has three electrons: two in the first shell and one in the second (written 2,1). The electronic structures of the first 20 elements were given in Figure 28.4.

29.4 Metals and the periodic table

You may use physical properties, Figure 11.2, or chemical properties, Figure 25.1, to decide whether an element is a metal or a non-metal, but electronic structure gives a better way.

A metal is an element in which the number of electrons in the outer shell is less than, or equal to, the period number.

By this definition over 80 of the elements are metals. It is a very large class. Substances are more metallic as the atomic number increases down a group; substances are less metallic as the atomic number increases across a period (left to right). The metals can be sub-divided into three:

(a) *s-block* (groups I and II). By their chemical properties these elements are metals, although they have low melting and boiling points and low densities for metals.
(b) *d-block* (transition elements and some others). By their physical properties these elements are metals. Their chemical properties do not always show that they are metallic but they do form cations. These transition metals are often catalysts, have several valencies and form coloured compounds.
(c) *p-block* (later members of groups III, IV and V). These are getting close to the borderline. They form cations but their melting points are fairly low.

The outer electrons of metal atoms in a crystal are shared by all the atoms in the crystal. These electrons do not belong just to one atom. Give these electrons a 'push' and you have an electric current. Warm a metal wire in a vacuum and the electrons can leave the wire and travel across the space, as in a television tube.

The chemical properties of metals also follow from their electronic structures. Metal atoms in a reaction tend to lose electrons to form cations, so metals are reducing agents, see Sections 24.6 and 24.7. As before, there are exceptions, and the nearer the element is to the diagonal line across the p-block the more likely you are to find problems in classifying it by its properties. For example, copper does not react with dilute sulphuric acid nor with dilute hydrochloric acid, while carbon tetrachloride (tetrachloromethane) is stable to water.

29.5 Non-metals and the periodic table

One way of deciding whether an element is a non-metal is by the following definition.

A non-metal is an element which has more electrons in its outer shell than its period number.

The non-metals are on the right in the periodic table and are separated from the metals by the diagonal line across the p-block, see Figure 29.1. There are only 21 non-metals by this definition, see Figure 17.1. Non-metals form covalent molecules, see Chapter 31. These covalent molecules only have weak forces of attraction for one another so the elements have low melting and boiling points. The covalent molecules pack together in crystals in many ways and so the class of non-metals contains more variety than the class of metals.

The chemical properties of non-metals also follow from their electronic structures. When non-metal atoms react with metals they gain electrons to form anions, so non-metals are oxidising agents, see Sections 24.6 and 24.7. When two non-metals react with one another they form a covalent compound.

29.6 Trends down the group

If you look at a group of metals on the left hand side of the table, the valency electron (or electrons) gets further away from the nucleus as the atomic number of the element increases, as in lithium 2,1, sodium 2,8,1, potassium 2,8,8,1 and so on (in group I). This valency electron is lost to the non-metal in reactions. The further it is from the nucleus, the less tightly it is held by the positive charge of the nucleus, and the more easily it can be lost. Therefore the reactivity of the metal increases as the atomic number increases; the element is more metallic and a better reducing agent, see Chapters 11 and 24. The reactivity of the elements in group I increases from lithium to sodium to potassium and so on.

If you look down a group of non-metals on the right hand side of the table, the electron (or electrons) to be held after reactions is further and further away and will be less tightly held. Therefore, the reactivity of the non-metal decreases as the atomic number increases; the element is a poorer example of a non-metal and not so good as an oxidising agent. The most reactive of the halogens (group VII) is fluorine (electronic structure 2,7), with chlorine, bromine and iodine being less and less reactive.

29.7 Trends across a period

Look at period 3 in the table: sodium, magnesium . . . How well does each of these elements combine with chlorine? The compounds are less and less ionic. This is shown by their melting points:

	NaCl	$MgCl_2$	$AlCl_3$	$SiCl_4$	PCl_3
(in °C)	800	710	180	-70	-110

As you go from left to right across the table the chlorides react more and more with water (called hydrolysis). The elements themselves are less and less metallic. There is a decrease in reactivity of the elements from group I to the middle of the table and then an increase up to group VII.

30

Ionic Bonding

30.1 Ways of bonding

There are three ways in which the atoms of elements may join together:

(a) If the two elements are a metal and a non-metal, that is to say from the left and the right sides of the periodic table, then they combine to form a compound by ionic bonding.
(b) If the two elements are both non-metals, that is to say they are both from the right side of the periodic table, they combine to form a compound by covalent bonding, see Chapter 31.
(c) If the two elements are both metals, that is to say they are both from the left side of the periodic table, they join together to form an alloy, by metallic bonding, see Chapter 11 and Sections 28.4, 29.4 and 32.3.

Group 0, the noble gases, do not form any compounds in simple experiments. They are only important because of their electronic structures: helium 2; neon 2,8; argon 2,8,8.

For an example of class (a), take sodium (group I) and chlorine (group VII). When sodium is put in water there is a violent reaction and the corrosive solution of sodium hydroxide that is produced is alkaline. Chlorine is a yellow-green, poisonous gas. It will dissolve in water and the solution is acidic. Both of these elements are dangerous unless used carefully.

Sodium will burn in chlorine, and the compound produced, sodium chloride, is an essential part of our diet. What a contrast there is between the elements and the compound! A very important change occurred when the atoms combined.

For an example of class (*b*), take carbon (group IV) and oxygen (group VI). Carbon is sometimes eaten – a bit of burnt toast won't harm you. Oxygen is the part of the air which is vital to our lives. Carbon will burn in oxygen giving carbon monoxide (which is actively poisonous) or carbon dioxide (too much will suffocate you but a little won't harm you).

These two compounds, sodium chloride and carbon dioxide, both have relative molecular masses of about 50 (carbon dioxide 44 and sodium chloride 58·5, see Section 35.2), but there is a great difference in their properties, see Figure 30.1.

	Sodium chloride	*Carbon dioxide*
State	solid	gas
Melting point	800 °C	−78 °C
Boiling point	1500 °C	−78 °C (sublimes)
Electrical conductivity of solution in water	high	low

Fig. 30.1. Two types of compound

There are many compounds like sodium chloride which can be made by the ionic bonding of elements from the two sides of the periodic table. There are even more compounds like carbon dioxide which can be made by the covalent bonding of two or more elements that are close together on the right hand side of the periodic table. A special branch of chemistry (organic chemistry) is needed to deal with most of the compounds of carbon, see Chapters 19 and 20.

The electronic structures of the elements are the vital information to guide you in deciding how elements combine, see Figure 30.2. In most reactions it is only the electrons in the outer shell of the atom that react. They are often called the valency electrons.

30.2 Compounds of metals and non-metals

Metals are on the left of the periodic table and non-metals on the right. They combine by ionic bonding. If you look at sodium and

	H							He
	1							2

He	Li	Be	B	C	N	O	F	Ne
2,0	2,1	2,2	2,3	2,4	2,5	2,6	2,7	2,8

Ne	Na	Mg	Al	Si	P	S	Cl	Ar
2,8,0	2,8,1	2,8,2	2,8,3	2,8,4	2,8,5	2,8,6	2,8,7	2,8,8

Ar	K	Ca
2,8,8,0	2,8,8,1	2,8,8,2

The noble gases are printed twice to help you realise that
metals forming ionic compounds lose electrons to go 'back' to the
electronic structure of the previous noble gas. Non-metals gain
electrons to go 'forwards' to the electronic structure of the next
noble gas. A line across the table divides metals on the left
from non-metals on the right.

Fig. 30.2.   The electronic structures of some elements

chlorine you see that sodium has the electronic structure 2,8,1 and
the nearest noble gas to it is neon with the electronic structure 2,8.
Chlorine has the electronic structure 2,8,7 and the nearest noble gas
to it is argon with the electronic structure 2,8,8. When sodium is
burnt in chlorine an electron is *transferred* from the sodium atom to
the chlorine atom.

The result of moving an electron from the sodium atom is to give
it the electronic structure of neon. It still has 11 protons in the
nucleus but it now has only 10 electrons so it has a positive charge of
1. It is a sodium ion, Na^+, a typical cation or positive ion.

The result of moving an electron to the chlorine atom is to give it
the electronic structure of argon. It still has 17 protons in the nucleus
but it now has 18 electrons so it has a negative charge of 1. It is a
chloride ion, Cl^-, a typical anion or negative ion.

One way of showing this in a diagram is to let a large dot or the
symbol stand for the nucleus of the atom. Small circles or small dots
and crosses can be used to stand for the electrons. This is to show
which atom the electrons come from (but all electrons are of course
identical). Large circles can be drawn round the nucleus to repre-
sent the energy levels of the electrons in their shells, see Figure 30.3.

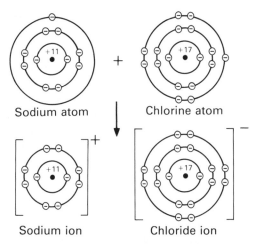

Fig. 30.3. The formation of the ionic compound, sodium chloride

A positive ion will attract a negative ion wherever they are. If the reaction of sodium and chlorine is carried out under dry conditions then the attraction gives you solid sodium chloride. In the solid the ions are arranged in a regular pattern – a **lattice**. It is like having two kinds of brick in a wall. The chloride ion is bigger than the sodium ion, see Figure 30.4(b). To our eyes the sodium chloride crystal

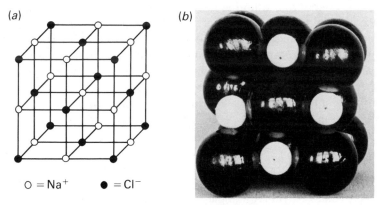

$O = Na^+$ $\bullet = Cl^-$

Fig. 30.4. The crystal pattern of sodium chloride (*a*) The ions are arranged in a lattice; (*b*) A 'space-filling' model, in which the ions are represented by spheres of different sizes

looks cubic. X-rays are used to find the pattern of the ions in the crystal.

Ionic bonding is the attraction of positive and negative ions for each other. This is a very strong form of bonding. The compounds have high melting points and boiling points. Ionic compounds, also called electrovalent compounds, are usually solids. The ions cannot move very far unless the compounds are melted. When the ions move, an electric current can be carried. Molten sodium chloride is an electrolyte. When the ions reach the electrodes in electrolysis, sodium atoms and chlorine molecules are formed again.

Ionic compounds are usually soluble in water. The solutions are also electrolytes but in electrolysis you may not get the original elements back again because different reactions occur at the electrodes (the selective discharge theory, see Section 14.2). Some ionic compounds are not soluble in water because the ions have multiple charges: the attractions of cations for anions are too strong to let the water molecules get between the ions, for example aluminium oxide, $(Al^{3+})_2(O^{2-})_3$.

30.3 Some more examples of ionic compounds

(a) Calcium chloride
Calcium has the electronic structure 2,8,8,2 and the nearest noble gas is argon 2,8,8. Chlorine has the electronic structure 2,8,7 and the nearest noble gas is again argon 2,8,8. When calcium combines with chlorine the calcium atom loses 2 electrons so the ion is Ca^{2+}. (How many protons are in a calcium atom, and how many in a calcium ion?) Two chlorine atoms react and each one receives one electron to give it the electronic structure of argon. Each of these chlorine atoms becomes a chloride ion, Cl^-. So a calcium chloride crystal is made up of $Ca^{2+} + 2Cl^-$ in a regular pattern. (Magnesium chloride is similar.)

(b) Calcium oxide
The electronic structures are

Ca	2,8,8,2	(nearest noble gas	Ar 2,8,8)
O	2,6	(nearest noble gas	Ne 2,8)

Transferring two electrons directly from a calcium atom to an oxygen atom gives the ions Ca^{2+} 2,8,8 and O^{2-} 2,6.

The higher charges of these ions cause the melting point to be 2500 °C. Calcium oxide is not very soluble in water even though it reacts to become calcium hydroxide. (Magnesium oxide is similar.)

(c) Sodium oxide
The electronic structures are

Na 2,8,1 (nearest noble gas Ne 2,8)
O   2,6   (nearest noble gas Ne 2,8)

The oxygen atom must gain two electrons to get the noble gas electronic structure, so two sodium atoms are needed. The sodium oxide crystal is therefore made up of $2Na^+ + O^{2-}$ in a regular pattern. All these ions have the electronic structure of neon. (Potassium oxide is similar.)

31

Covalent Bonding

31.1 Elements forming covalent molecules

The non-metallic elements on the right hand side of the periodic table combine with one another by sharing electrons between atoms. Usually one electron is supplied by each atom. Then the atoms have the same electronic structures as the nearest noble gases. It is possible to talk about a definite bond between the atoms. The bond is a shared pair of electrons; a double bond is two shared pairs of electrons.

Hydrogen behaves as a non-metal in many compounds studied at this stage. Hydrogen, atomic number 1, has the simplest atom of all elements. It has one electron going round the nucleus. The nearest noble gas is helium, of electronic structure 2. Hydrogen atoms normally travel around in pairs, called molecules. The two atoms are joined by a covalent bond, see Figure 31.1. By sharing electrons, each hydrogen atom gains the electronic structure of helium. A convenient abbreviation is to let the element symbol stand for the nucleus of the atom and the inner electrons, so you only draw the outer (or valency) electrons. Yet another way of drawing a molecule is to draw the bonds between the atoms as dashes, for example H–H, see Figure 31.1.

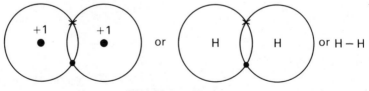

Fig. 31.1. Hydrogen

Chlorine atoms also go in pairs. By sharing electrons, each chlorine atom has the electronic structure of argon, see Figure 31.2. The chlorine molecule is an example of the 'octet' theory: most atoms gain eight electrons in the outermost shell when they combine to form molecules or when they form ions.

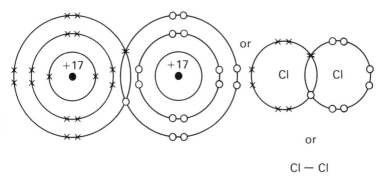

Fig. 31.2. Chlorine

Oxygen and nitrogen also form diatomic molecules. Ozone (O_3, trioxygen) is triatomic. White phosphorus is tetra-atomic (P_4, in a tetrahedron). Rhombic and monoclinic sulphur are octa-atomic (S_8, in a ring). Oxygen, O_2, is an example of a molecule that should conform to the octet theory but does not. The structure of oxygen is not $O = O$ as suggested in Figure 31.3 because oxygen is too reactive and also has unusual magnetic properties. There are a few elements that do not keep to the octet theory because their nearest noble gas is helium (which has only two electrons).

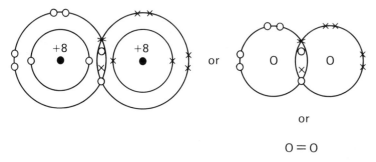

Fig. 31.3. An oxygen molecule (according to the octet theory)

31.2 Non-metals in compounds

(a) Hydrogen chloride

Chlorine has the electronic structure 2,8,7 and the nearest noble gas to it is argon of electronic structure 2,8,8.

When hydrogen combines with chlorine to give the gas hydrogen chloride, the hydrogen atom shares its electron with the unpaired electron in the third shell of the chlorine atom. By sharing, the hydrogen atom has two electrons (like helium) and the chlorine atom has 2,8,8 electrons (like argon), see Figure 31.4.

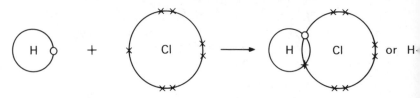

Fig. 31.4.   The covalent compound, hydrogen chloride

Hydrogen chloride is a gas (boiling point −85 °C). If it is dissolved in methylbenzene the solution is a non-electrolyte. Unlike many covalent compounds it will dissolve in water. When it dissolves in water it becomes an ionic compound, hydrochloric acid.

(b) Water

Hydrogen has the electronic structure 1 and oxygen has the electronic structure 2,6. Two hydrogen atoms combine with one oxygen atom to give water. Each hydrogen atom becomes like helium (2) and the oxygen atom like neon (2,8) in electronic structure, see Figure 31.5.

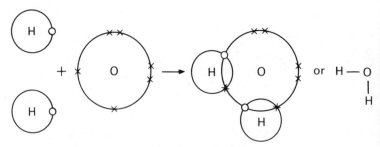

Fig. 31.5.   Water

(c) Ammonia

Hydrogen has the electronic structure 1 (it becomes like He 2) and nitrogen has the electronic structure 2,5 (it becomes like Ne 2,8). Three hydrogen atoms combine with one nitrogen atom to give ammonia, see Figure 31.6.

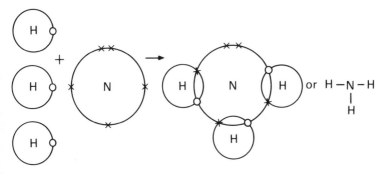

Fig. 31.6. Ammonia

(d) Methane

Hydrogen has the electronic structure 1 (it becomes like He 2) and carbon has the electronic structure 2,4 (it becomes like Ne 2,8). Four hydrogen atoms combine with one carbon atom to give methane, see Figure 31.7.

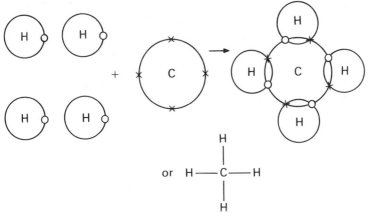

Fig. 31.7. Methane

31.3 More complex covalent compounds

(a) Ethanol

The electronic structures are

H 1   (it becomes like He 2)
C 2,4   (it becomes like Ne 2,8)
O 2,6   (it becomes like Ne 2,8)

There are six hydrogen atoms, two carbon atoms and one oxygen atom in a molecule of ethanol, see Figure 31.8.

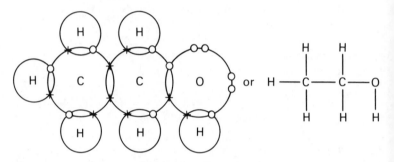

Fig. 31.8. Ethanol

(b) Carbon dioxide

The electronic structures are

C 2,4   (it becomes like Ne 2,8)
O 2,6   (it becomes like Ne 2,8)

A molecule of carbon dioxide has one carbon atom and two oxygen atoms, see Figure 31.9. The oxygen atoms are linked by two double bonds, four electrons each, to the carbon.

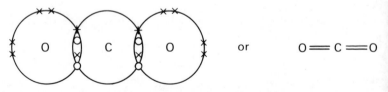

Fig. 31.9. Carbon dioxide

31.4 Properties of covalent substances

The atoms in a covalent molecule are joined together. What holds the separate molecules together? The simple answer is 'not a lot'. At high temperatures, molecules which collide bounce off one another. At low temperatures the molecules may stick together so that a liquid or a solid is formed. There is a tiny force of attraction between one molecule and the next which only operates effectively at low temperatures. This force was first described by Johannes van der Waals (1837–1923, Netherlands). It can be described generally as the slight attraction of the nucleus of an atom in one molecule for the electrons of an atom in the next molecule.

Substances which are made up of *small* covalent molecules have low melting points and low boiling points because the van der Waals' forces between separate molecules are weak.

There are molecules, not ions, in covalent substances and so the substances are non-electrolytes: they do not conduct electricity when they are melted or when they are dissolved in water. There are exceptions to this statement: for example, hydrogen chloride is a covalent gas which dissolves in water and becomes an ionic substance, hydrochloric acid. Change of structure causes a change of properties.

Many covalent substances are not soluble in water. They are soluble in other (non-aqueous) solvents such as ethanol ('alcohol' in methylated spirit), 1,1,1-trichloroethane (in Liquid Paper), propanone (also called acetone, nail varnish remover), white spirit (some paints), paraffin, petrol and so on.

The general properties of covalent compounds are often the opposite of those of ionic compounds, see Figure 31.10. Ionic compounds are formed by elements far away from each other in the periodic table, for example sodium and chlorine. When two elements close together on the right hand side of the periodic table combine the compound is covalent. Between these two extreme cases it is often hard to decide whether a compound is covalent or ionic.

	Ionic substances	*Covalent substances*
Formation	electrons are transferred from metal atoms to non-metal atoms	electrons are shared between atoms of non-metals
Typical examples	$NaCl$, Na_2O, $MgCl_2$, MgO, $CaCl_2$, CaO, $NaOH$, $HCl(aq)$	H_2, O_2, N_2, Cl_2, $HCl(g)$, H_2O, NH_3, CH_4, CO_2, C_2H_4
Melting point	high	low
Boiling point	high	low
Usual state seen	solid	gas or liquid, some are solids (if high relative molecular mass)
Crystal structure	this depends on the relative sizes and the charges on the ions	this depends on the shapes of molecules and on the positions of the different elements in the molecules
Crystal forces	strong, electrostatic forces between ions	weak, van der Waals' forces between molecules
Solvents	water	often not water
Electrolysis	this is possible when they are melted or dissolved in water: they are electrolytes	non-electrolytes

Fig. 31.10. Ionic and covalent substances

31.5 Giant molecules

Covalent bonding can join many atoms together to form giant molecules. They are sometimes called macromolecules. The simplest examples are the allotropes of carbon, diamond and graphite, see Sections 17.8 and 32.4.

Many natural and synthetic substances are made up of giant molecules: sand (SiO_2), proteins, starch, rubber and polymers, see Chapter 20.

The properties of covalent substances which have giant molecules are not the same as the properties of covalent substances which are made up of small molecules. A substance made of macromolecules has a high melting point and boiling point compared to a substance which is made of small covalent molecules. A substance may decompose (break up) before it melts because the covalent bonds between the atoms break on heating.

Ion exchange resins, used to soften water, are plastics which contain anions that are giant structures linked by covalent bonding, together with small cations. The cations are mobile and are exchanged for the calcium ions in the hard water, see Section 3.2.

31.6 The shapes of molecules

It is easy to draw all molecules as if they are flat and the bonds at right angles. In real life, all covalent molecules have a definite shape and the shape may be important when you are trying to explain the properties of a substance.

A water molecule is V-shaped so it is better to draw it as in Figure 31.5 rather than as a straight line H—O—H. An ammonia molecule is pyramidal and a methane molecule tetrahedral, see Figure 31.11.

The shapes of organic molecules are important. For example, the properties of haemoglobin, rubber, plastics and fibres cannot be explained just by knowing what elements they contain or even in what order the atoms are linked.

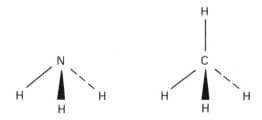

Fig. 31.11. Ammonia and methane molecules

32

Crystals

32.1 Making crystals

When a liquid or a solution cools you may see small pieces of a solid
forming. Look carefully at the solid and you may see that most of
the pieces have the same shape. The pieces may be large or small but
the corners have the same angles. The small pieces of the solid are
called **crystals**. The faces (sides) of the crystals are flat. Often lots of

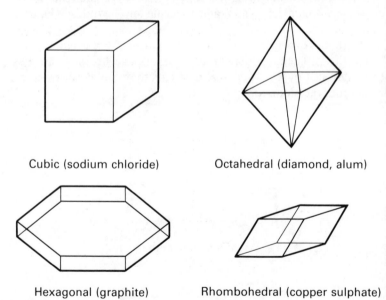

Cubic (sodium chloride)   Octahedral (diamond, alum)

Hexagonal (graphite)   Rhombohedral (copper sulphate)

Fig. 32.1.   Typical crystal shapes

tiny crystals join together and it is hard to see what is their individual shape. Take a large crystal, press a knife on it and see if the solid splits (cleaves). It may be easier to split the solid in some directions than others (it's like the grain of wood). Some typical crystal shapes are shown in Figure 32.1.

Crystals are solids with these properties:

(*a*) flat faces and straight edges;
(*b*) constant angles between faces;
(*c*) definite shape;
(*d*) can be split into smaller crystals.

When an impurity is added to a liquid substance or a solution the crystals that you get may not have their usual shape.

32.2 Growing big crystals

This needs a lot of patience. If you warm some water and tip powdered alum into it, lots of the solid will dissolve. When no more will dissolve, decant the saturated solution into a clean beaker and cover it with a piece of paper with a few holes in it. Let the beaker cool slowly. Even when it is at room temperature water will continue to evaporate. After some hours or even days you will have some alum crystals.

Take a good crystal and hang it by a piece of cotton in the middle of a warm solution of alum, see Figure 32.2. As the solution cools

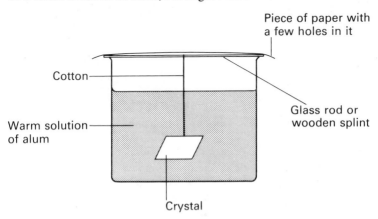

Fig. 32.2. Growing a large crystal

the crystal will grow. (If you are unlucky the specimen crystal dissolves or you get a lot of small crystals again.)

The full name of alum is aluminium potassium sulphate-12-water. Many crystals that are obtained from aqueous solutions trap some water in them and that is shown by their full names. They are said to be **hydrated**; they contain **water of crystallisation**. To find out how much water is in such crystals, see Section 35.6.

Some substances crystallise without any water of crystallisation: they are said to be **anhydrous**. Common salt (sodium chloride) and sodium nitrate crystals are anhydrous.

32.3 Metals

Four-fifths of the elements are metals. Nearly all the metals have one of the following three crystal structures.

(*a*) *Body-centred cubic*, see Figure 32.3. A typical atom such as the one at the centre has eight near neighbours. Two elements that crystallise in this pattern are iron and sodium.

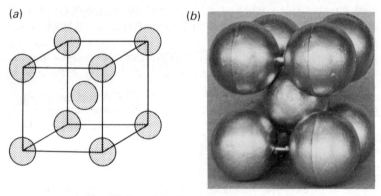

(*a*)   (*b*)

Fig. 32.3.   A body-centred cubic crystal

(*b*) *Cubic close-packed* or *face-centred cubic*. A typical atom in this type of crystal has twelve near neighbours. Two elements that crystallise in this pattern are copper and aluminium.

(*c*) *Hexagonal close-packed*. A typical atom in this type of crystal also has twelve near neighbours. Elements that crystallise in this pattern are zinc and magnesium.

32.4 Allotropy

Some elements can crystallise in several ways. Each type of crystal shape is called an **allotrope**.

Allotropy is the existence of an element in two or more distinct crystalline forms.

For example, carbon can crystallise in hexagons as graphite or in octahedrons as diamond, see Figure 17.6. Graphite is more stable than diamond but the difference in energy is very small. If you heat diamonds in an electric furnace you get graphite. It is possible, but difficult, to make graphite into diamonds. The physical properties of diamond and graphite are different, see Section 17.8. The chemical properties are the same but it is harder to make diamonds burn than graphite. The charcoals are kinds of carbon which do not have any obvious crystalline shape.

Sulphur shows a different type of allotropy. If sulphur is crystallised at low temperatures the crystals are rhombic; if it is crystallised at high temperatures the crystals are monoclinic. The important temperature which divides the two types of crystals is 96 °C (the **transition** temperature). In this kind of allotropy it is fairly easy to change one type of crystal into the other: you just raise or lower the temperature at which you make the crystals. The physical properties of the two types of sulphur crystals are not very different, see Section 17.6; their chemical properties are identical.

Compounds can also crystallise in several ways. Thus calcium carbonate can crystallise as the mineral calcite, found in chalk, limestone and marble, or as the mineral aragonite.

32.5 Inside a crystal

The fact that a crystal has a regular (definite) shape points to the arrangement of the particles that make up the crystal. In the same way you might say that the symmetry of a wall points to the symmetry of the bricks from which it is made. A crystal is an ordered pattern of particles. The pattern has to be found by using X-rays because the particles are so small (about a ten millionth of a millimetre in diameter).

Structure	Melting point	Density	Electrical conductivity	Solubility in water
Atoms of a metallic element	high	high	high	low, unless a chemical reaction occurs
Atoms or small molecules of a non-metallic element or Molecules of a simple covalent compound	low	low	none	as above
Molecules of a macromolecular element or compound	high or medium	medium or low	none	as above
Ions of an ionic solid	high	medium	none when solid; high if melted or dissolved in water	usually high

Fig. 32.4. The general properties of substances according to their structures

We can find out what sort of particles there are in a crystal by studying the properties of the solid, see Figure 32.4. For the properties of metallic and non-metallic elements in detail, see Figure 11.2; for ionic and covalent compounds, see Figure 31.10.

Now, using Figure 32.4, try to decide in which class to put the following substances. (Answers on page 268.)

Substance	Melting point (°C)	Density (in g/ml)	Electrical conductivity	Solubility in water
A	3 700	3·5	none	none
B	800	2·1	high when melted or dissolved in water	medium
C	1 535	7·9	high	none
D	119	2·1	none	none
E	0	0·9	none	infinite
F	118	1·0	low (in water)	high
G	−77	0·000 76	low (in water)	high

33

Symbols and Formulae

33.1 Symbols

A symbol can be used as an abbreviation for an element. It is usually one or two letters; only the first is a capital letter. The symbol stands for one atom of the element. Sometimes the symbol is obvious:

O for oxygen	S for sulphur
N for nitrogen	H for hydrogen
Al for aluminium	Ca for calcium

Sometimes it is not quite so obvious:

Cl for chlorine	Cr for chromium
Zn for zinc	Mg for magnesium

The symbol may come from a Latin word or from another language:

Cu for copper	Fe for iron
Ag for silver	Pb for lead
Na for sodium	K for potassium

33.2 Atoms and molecules

Atoms can exist on their own. This is true for all metals and the noble gases (helium, neon, argon . . .). In some elements and all covalent compounds, atoms are joined together in molecules. The atoms of many common non-metallic elements are normally in pairs: oxygen, hydrogen, nitrogen and chlorine. For these elements we write the formulae O_2, H_2, N_2 and Cl_2. The number of atoms in a molecule (its atomicity) is written smaller, below and to the right of the symbol.

33.3 Valency

The valency of an element is the number of hydrogen atoms which will combine with (or replace) one atom of the element. Hydrogen has a valency of one.

In the compound hydrogen chloride, an atom of hydrogen has combined with an atom of chlorine. Hydrogen and chlorine normally exist as molecules, each consisting of two atoms. The minimum quantity of each element you can use is one molecule, so when they react you get two molecules of hydrogen chloride, see Figure 33.1. The valency of chlorine is one. The formula of hydrogen chloride is HCl. (The figure one is not written by each symbol but is implied.) The atom of hydrogen in a molecule of hydrogen chloride can be replaced by an atom of sodium, so sodium chloride is NaCl. The valency of sodium is one.

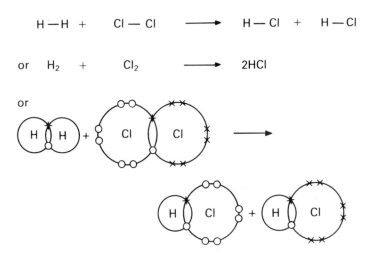

Figure 33.1. The combination of hydrogen and chlorine can be written in several ways

Two atoms of hydrogen combined with one atom of oxygen give one molecule of hydrogen oxide (better known as water, H_2O). The valency of oxygen is two. Try writing an equation for the reaction of hydrogen and oxygen molecules.

To be able to write formulae you need to know the valencies of elements, see Figure 33.2. When you consider the modern atomic theory you find that the valency of an element is the number of covalent bonds formed by an atom or else the charge on the ion which is formed.

Valencies of hydrogen and some common metals

1	2	3
hydrogen, H	magnesium, Mg	aluminium, Al
sodium, Na	calcium, Ca	iron, Fe
potassium, K	barium, Ba	
silver, Ag	iron, Fe	
	copper, Cu	
	zinc, Zn	
	lead, Pb	

Valencies of some common non-metals

1	2	3	4
chlorine, Cl	oxygen, O	nitrogen, N	carbon, C
bromine, Br	sulphur, S		sulphur, S
iodine, I	carbon, C		

Fig. 33.2.   Valencies of elements

To help you learn these valencies you can make a paper jigsaw to work the formulae of substances. The metals are given prongs and the non-metals dents, see Figure 33.3. The aim is to match the pieces to get the formulae.

Some elements have more than one valency. To help you to know which valency is used, the valency of a metal may be written in Roman numbers straight after the name. For example, iron(II) sulphide is FeS and iron(III) sulphide is Fe_2S_3.

If the compound contains only non-metals, then the name may

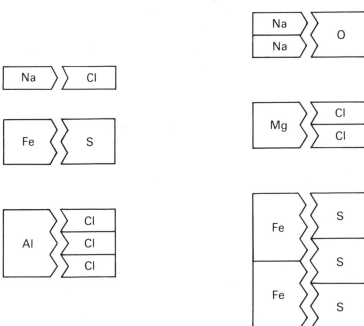

Fig. 33.3. Using jigsaw pieces to work out formulae

Valency of a metallic radical

1
ammonium, NH_4 (This behaves like a metal because it forms positive ions.)

Valencies of some common non-metallic radicals

1	2
hydroxide, OH	sulphate, SO_4
nitrate, NO_3	sulphite, SO_3
hydrogencarbonate, HCO_3	carbonate, CO_3
hydrogensulphate, HSO_4	
chlorate(I), often called hypochlorite, ClO	
chlorate(V), often just called chlorate, ClO_3	

Fig. 33.4. Valencies of radicals

tell you the numbers of each kind of atom and of the valencies being used. For example, in carbon monoxide, CO, carbon has a valency of 2, but in carbon dioxide, CO_2, carbon has a valency of 4.

33.4 Radicals

Some atoms are often found together in compounds – these sets of atoms are called radicals. Radicals usually cannot exist on their own. For example, a sulphur atom with four atoms of oxygen is called a sulphate radical and it has a valency of two. For the valencies of some common radicals see Figure 33.4.

To work out the formulae of compounds containing radicals you can make more jigsaw pieces. Sometimes brackets are needed to show that several radicals are included in a formula:

sodium nitrate is $NaNO_3$
zinc nitrate is $Zn(NO_3)_2$
aluminium nitrate is $Al(NO_3)_3$

The 2 in the formula of zinc nitrate multiplies the numbers of both kinds of atoms in the bracket (as in mathematics). The formula could be written ZnN_2O_6 but it would not be so obvious that it was a nitrate, an NO_3 compound. No brackets are necessary if there is only one radical in a formula; look at these examples:

ammonium chloride NH_4Cl
ammonium sulphate $(NH_4)_2SO_4$
iron(II) sulphate $FeSO_4$
iron(III) sulphate $Fe_2(SO_4)_3$

Acids are hydrogen compounds in which the hydrogen can be replaced by a metal. They only behave as acids when dissolved in water. Their names partly hide their formulae:

hydrochloric acid is hydrogen chloride in water, HCl,
nitric acid is hydrogen nitrate in water, HNO_3,
and sulphuric acid is hydrogen sulphate (two words, unlike above) in water, H_2SO_4

For more ideas about valency see Chapters 30 and 31.

34

Equations

34.1 Describing reactions in words

Charcoal and coke are mostly carbon. They will burn in oxygen or air to give carbon dioxide. In words you can write:

$$\text{carbon} + \text{oxygen} \rightarrow \text{carbon dioxide}$$

This is an equation in words. It tells you what you start with and what is given by the reaction. It does not tell you whether you need to heat the coke to start the combustion or how much energy is given out in the reaction.

An equation is a sort of shorthand because it gives a quick summary of what happens in a reaction. An equation does not tell you what you will see, but you can improve it by adding the state symbols: (s) for a solid, (l) for a liquid, (aq) for a solution in water (Latin *aqua*) and (g) for a gas. So you could write:

$$\text{carbon(s)} + \text{oxygen(g)} \rightarrow \text{carbon dioxide(g)}$$

Sometimes it is helpful to write the colours of substances under an equation:

$$\text{carbon(s)} + \text{oxygen(g)} \rightarrow \text{carbon dioxide(g)}$$
black

You may leave a blank if a substance is colourless.

Note: 'white is crushed colourless'. An ice cube from the fridge may be clear (transparent) and colourless: you can see through it. If you smash the ice cube into lots of tiny pieces you may say it is white. The same is true of lots of substances. A large perfect crystal is transparent and may be colourless: lots of tiny crystals are white and either translucent (they will let light through but you can't see through them) or opaque (no light passes through, and you can't see through). Classify the following substances as transparent, translucent or opaque: a car windscreen, a kitchen tile, frosted glass. (Answers on page 268.)

Here are some other examples of equations in words. Try to add the state symbols and colours or even translate them into formulae. (Answers on page 268.)

(*a*) sodium hydroxide + hydrochloric acid → sodium chloride + water

(*b*) calcium carbonate → calcium oxide + carbon dioxide

(*c*) hydrogen peroxide → water + oxygen

(*d*) sodium hydrogencarbonate → sodium carbonate + water + carbon dioxide

(*e*) ammonium chloride + sodium hydroxide → sodium chloride + water + ammonia

It may be helpful to write equations so that the left and right sides are in a similar order. So you may like to write substances in the order

solids, liquids, solutions, gases

or

base + acid → salt + water

In some books equations are written with an equals sign. Using an arrow shows the direction of a chemical reaction. If a reaction can go forwards or backwards then it is described as reversible and two half arrows ⇌ are used. If the conditions have to be changed to make it reversible then two full arrows are used ⇄.

34.2 Describing equations in symbols

An equation in words can be shortened to an equation using the formulae of substances. The combustion of charcoal or coke can be written as

$$C \quad + O_2 \quad \rightarrow CO_2$$

or as

$$C(s) + O_2(g) \rightarrow CO_2(g)$$

Equations are written for molecules of substances, so you must write O_2 for oxygen because that is how the atoms usually travel around.

Equations can be written without knowing whether substances are ionic or covalent. You can write NaCl for sodium chloride rather than $Na^+ + Cl^-$. Water is mostly covalent and the few H^+ and OH^- in it are usually ignored.

Here are some examples of equations in symbols. Try to add the state symbols. (Answers on page 268.)

(a) $NaOH \quad + \quad HNO_3 \quad \rightarrow NaNO_3 \quad + H_2O$
(b) $Ca(OH)_2 \quad + \quad CO_2 \quad \rightarrow CaCO_3 \quad + H_2O$
(c) $NaHCO_3 \quad + \quad HCl \quad \rightarrow NaCl \quad + H_2O \quad + CO_2$
(d) $AgNO_3 \quad + \quad KCl \quad \rightarrow AgCl \quad + KNO_3$
(e) $BaCl_2 \quad + \quad MgSO_4 \rightarrow BaSO_4 \quad + MgCl_2$

34.3 Balancing equations

The equation in words for calcium carbonate dissolving in hydrochloric acid is:

calcium carbonate + hydrochloric acid → calcium chloride + water + carbon dioxide

This can be changed into a statement in symbols:

$$CaCO_3 + HCl \rightarrow CaCl_2 + H_2O + CO_2$$

Now, count the atoms on each side of the arrow:

	Left	Right
calcium, Ca	1	1
carbon, C	1	1
oxygen, O	3	3
hydrogen, H	1	2
chlorine, Cl	1	2

You can see that there are not enough hydrogen and chlorine atoms on the left hand side. To balance the statement you need two hydrochloric acid molecules.

$$CaCO_3 + 2HCl \rightarrow CaCl_2 + H_2O + CO_2$$

or $CaCO_3(s) + 2HCl(aq) \rightarrow CaCl_2(aq) + H_2O(l) + CO_2(g)$

You must *never* adjust the formula of a substance to balance a statement. The formula of a substance is fixed by the valencies of the elements. You must only adjust the numbers of units (atoms or molecules) of the substance.

Sometimes more than one alteration must be made to balance a statement. For example, count the atoms for this statement about sodium reacting with water:

$$Na + H_2O \rightarrow NaOH + H_2$$

	Left	Right
sodium, Na	1	1
hydrogen, H	2	3
oxygen, O	1	1

The hydrogen atoms on the left hand side are in twos, in the water molecule. So the first step is to get them in twos on the right hand side.

$$Na + H_2O \rightarrow 2NaOH + H_2$$

Then you see that the sodium atoms are not balanced, so a second step gives you:

$$2Na + H_2O \rightarrow 2NaOH + H_2$$

Thirdly you may see that the oxygen atoms and the hydrogen atoms are not balanced:

$$2Na + 2H_2O \rightarrow 2NaOH + H_2$$

Now you have a balanced equation. It is better to call the stages 'statements' rather than equations. Balancing a statement to give an equation is a way of showing the law of conservation of mass. To be accurate, if it is an equation then it must be balanced. Trial and error are the only way to do the balancing. Equations are not items you should sit down and learn off by heart. Get some practice by trying to balance the following statements (you can also add the state symbols). (Answers on page 268.)

(a) $NaOH$ $+ H_2SO_4$ $\rightarrow Na_2SO_4$ $+ H_2O$

(b) Na_2CO_3 $+ HNO_3$ $\rightarrow NaNO_3$ $+ H_2O$ $+ CO_2$

(c) Fe_3O_4 $+ CO$ $\rightarrow Fe$ $+ CO_2$

(d) CuO $+ CH_4$ $\rightarrow Cu$ $+ H_2O$ $+ CO_2$

(e) Mg $+ O_2$ $\rightarrow MgO$

34.4 Ionic equations

All acids, alkalis and salts in dilute aqueous solution are ionic.

This important statement can be applied to many of the reactions you study. The equation for the neutralisation of sodium hydroxide with hydrochloric acid is:

$$NaOH(aq) + HCl(aq) \rightarrow NaCl(aq) + H_2O(l)$$

Now use the statement above. Remember that metals form positive ions and non-metals form negative ions, and that the number of charges depends on the valency, see Figures 33.2 and 33.4.

$$Na^+ + OH^- + H^+ + Cl^- \rightarrow Na^+ + Cl^- + H_2O$$

Water is written as a covalent molecule because the proportion of ions is very, very small. The sodium and chloride ions are on each side of the equation and so can be cancelled out. They are **spectator** ions. They do not change at all in the reaction.

This leaves you with the vital part of the equation:

$$H^+ + OH^- \rightarrow H_2O$$

Cations are usually written before anions. Unless the solution is evaporated, the sodium ions do not combine with the chloride ions, so they cannot be said to react. The essential part of the reaction is that hydrogen ions from an acid react with hydroxide ions from an alkali to give molecules of water. So the energy change (57 kJ per mole of water formed) when a strong acid reacts with a strong base is always the same.

When sodium hydroxide solution is added to copper(II) sulphate solution the full equation is

$$CuSO_4(aq) + 2NaOH(aq) \rightarrow Cu(OH)_2(s) + Na_2SO_4(aq)$$

You should be able to show that the ionic equation is:

$$Cu^{2+} + 2OH^- \rightarrow Cu(OH)_2$$

Any copper salt in solution with any alkali will give a precipitate of copper(II) hydroxide. For ion–electron equations see Section 24.7 and Chapter 14.

35

Molar Masses

35.1 Relative atomic masses

Atoms of different elements have different masses. Dalton stressed this in his atomic theory. Hydrogen has the lightest atom: we can call its mass 1 and compare it with other elements. An oxygen atom is 16 times as heavy and a carbon atom is 12 times as heavy as a hydrogen atom. Atomic masses can be compared to one another,

Element	Symbol	Relative atomic mass	Element	Symbol	Relative atomic mass
Aluminium	Al	27	Magnesium	Mg	24
Argon	Ar	40	Manganese	Mn	55
Barium	Ba	137	Mercury	Hg	201
Bromine	Br	80	Nitrogen	N	14
Calcium	Ca	40	Oxygen	O	16
Carbon	C	12	Phosphorus	P	31
Chlorine	Cl	35·5	Potassium	K	39
Chromium	Cr	52	Silicon	Si	28
Copper	Cu	64	Silver	Ag	108
Fluorine	F	19	Sodium	Na	23
Helium	He	4	Sulphur	S	32
Hydrogen	H	1	Titanium	Ti	48
Iodine	I	127	Uranium	U	238
Iron	Fe	56	Zinc	Zn	65
Lead	Pb	207			

Fig. 35.1. The symbols and relative atomic masses of some common elements

rather than weighed in grams like sweets in a shop. That is why they are called *relative* atomic masses. They are ratios (numbers) and do not have units.

The relative atomic mass of an element is the average mass of its atoms compared to a carbon-12 atom, which is taken as 12. Its symbol is A_r.

The definition relates elements to carbon because carbon forms more compounds than any other element. This gives scientists a better start for finding out the values of relative atomic masses.

Except for chlorine ($A_r = 35 \cdot 5$) the relative atomic mass of an element can be taken as a whole number, see Figure 35.1. These values are always given for calculations if they are needed – you don't have to remember them.

35.2 Relative molecular masses

The relative molecular mass of an element or a compound is the average mass of its molecules compared to a carbon-12 atom which is taken as 12. Its symbol is M_r.

Like the relative atomic mass, it is a ratio and does not have units. In calculations it is found by adding up the relative atomic masses of the elements, according to the formula of the substance.

(a) $M_r(H_2)$ $= 1 \times 2$ $= \quad 2$

(b) $M_r(H_2O)$ $= (1 \times 2)$ $+ (16 \times 1)$ $= \quad 18$

(c) $M_r(H_2SO_4)$ $= (1 \times 2)$ $+ (32 \times 1)$ $+ (16 \times 4) = \quad 98$

(d) $M_r(NaOH)$ $= (23 \times 1)$ $+ (16 \times 1)$ $+ (1 \times 1) = \quad 40$

(e) $M_r(CuSO_4 \cdot 5H_2O) = (64 \times 1)$ $+ (32 \times 1)$ $+ (16 \times 4)$
                                  $+5[(1 \times 2) + (16 \times 1)]$ $= 250$

(f) $M_r(SO_4^{2-})$ $= (32 \times 1)$ $+ (16 \times 4)$ $= \quad 96$

Hydrogen is the standard for comparing the densities of gases, see Section 17.9. You can measure the density of a gaseous substance and divide it by the density of hydrogen. If you double the answer you get the relative molecular mass of the substance. This is a useful way of checking the formula of a substance, see Section 35.5.

35.3 Molar masses

The molar mass of an element or compound is the relative molecular mass of the substance in grams. Its symbol is M.

The molar mass of an element or compound contains as many particles as there are atoms in 12 g of carbon-12. There are $6 \cdot 02 \times 10^{23}$ atoms, that is to say there are

$$602\ 000\ 000\ 000\ 000\ 000\ 000\ 000$$

atoms in 12 g of carbon-12. This amount (quantity) is called a **mole** (abbreviation mol) of carbon-12. The molar mass of any element or compound contains this huge amount of particles, also called the **Avogadro constant** (Amedeo Avogadro, 1776–1856, Italy).

The mole is a huge amount (sometimes incorrectly called a number) of atoms, molecules or ions because these particles are individually very, very small. 2 g of hydrogen molecules, H_2, is one mole of hydrogen molecules and contains $6 \cdot 02 \times 10^{23}$ molecules. 18 g of water, H_2O, (about four teaspoonsful) is one mole of water molecules and contains $6 \cdot 02 \times 10^{23}$ molecules.

The mole is the chemists' unit of amount. A chemist does not count in dozens, thousands, or even millions, he or she counts in moles which are six hundred and two thousand million million millions at a time. The molar masses of the substances in Section 35.2 are:

(a)	$M(H_2)$	=	2 g/mol	(d) $M(NaOH)$	=	40 g/mol
(b)	$M(H_2O)$	=	18 g/mol	(e) $M(CuSO_4 \cdot 5H_2O)$	=	250 g/mol
(c)	$M(H_2SO_4)$	=	98 g/mol	(f) $M(SO_4^{2-})$	=	96 g/mol

The particles in calculations may be atoms, molecules or ions. You must state carefully which particles you are talking about when giving amounts of substances in moles. For quick sums the Avogadro constant may be taken to be 6×10^{23} particles in a mole.

In the chemical reactions you study you are doing experiments with moles of substances. To do calculations in moles keeps the numbers much smaller than counting the numbers of molecules.

The amount of a substance in moles is equal to its mass in grams divided by its molar mass in g/mol. For sodium atoms (Na) the molar mass is 23 g/mol, so if you had 2·3 g of sodium atoms you would have 2·3/23, that is to say 0·1 mole.

One mole of water molecules weighs 18 g, so 9 g of water is 0·5 mol, 6 g of water is 0·33 mol and so on. 1 kg of water is 1000/18 = 55·5 mol of water.

Remember:

$$\text{amount of substance (in moles)} = \frac{\text{mass of substance (in grams)}}{\text{molar mass of substance (in g/mol)}}$$

35.4 Reacting masses

The equation for the synthesis of water is

$$2H_2 + O_2 \rightarrow 2H_2O$$

The equation tells us that 2 molecules of hydrogen combine with 1 molecule of oxygen to give 2 molecules of water. You could multiply every item by $6·02 \times 10^{23}$ so the equation is also telling you that 2 mol of hydrogen combine with 1 mol of oxygen to give 2 mol of water.

The equation for the neutralisation of sodium hydroxide with hydrochloric acid is

$$NaOH + HCl \rightarrow NaCl + H_2O$$

As before, you can scale up this equation to think of 1 mol of sodium hydroxide reacting with 1 mol of hydrochloric acid to give 1 mol of sodium chloride and 1 mol of water.

If you think of equations as dealing with moles of substances instead of molecules of substances, you can calculate the masses of the substances involved.

$2H_2(g)$ + $O_2(g)$ $\rightarrow$ $2H_2O(l)$
4 g   32 g   36 g

$NaOH(aq)$ + $HCl(aq)$ $\rightarrow$ $NaCl(aq)$ + $H_2O(l)$
40 g   36·5 g   58·5 g   18 g

In many experiments you may have fractions or multiples of these masses. So, for example,

1 g of hydrogen reacts with 8 g of oxygen to give 9 g of water,

and

80 g of sodium hydroxide in solution reacts with 73 g of hydrogen chloride in solution (hydrochloric acid) to give 117 g of sodium chloride in solution and 36 g of water (extra).

If you know the molar masses of substances and you find the amounts that react, then you can work out the equation for the reaction. For example, with litmus as an indicator, 80 g of sodium hydroxide in solution react with 98 g of sulphuric acid (as a solution) to give 142 g of sodium sulphate and 36 g of water (extra). The molar masses are 40 g/mol, 98 g/mol, 142 g/mol and 18 g/mol respectively, so

> 2 mol of sodium hydroxide and 1 mol of sulphuric acid give 1 mol of sodium sulphate and 2 mol of water.

> Therefore the equation is

$$2NaOH(aq) + H_2SO_4(aq) \rightarrow Na_2SO_4(aq) + 2H_2O(l)$$

Here are some problems for you to solve. (Answers on page 269.)

(a) Write the equation in symbols for calcium carbonate decomposing to give calcium oxide and carbon dioxide. What amount (in moles) of each substance is produced if you start with 10 g of calcium carbonate? What masses of products are formed?

(b) Write the equation in symbols for the neutralisation of potassium hydroxide with nitric acid. What amount (in moles) of each substance is involved if you start with 2·8 g of potassium hydroxide? What mass of potassium nitrate should you be able to make?

(c) A manufacturer starts with 32 tonnes of sulphur (a tonne is one million grams). Sulphuric acid can be made by the contact process as shown in the following equations.

$$S(s) \quad + \ O_2(g) \quad \rightarrow \ SO_2(g)$$
$$2SO_2(g) \ + \ O_2(g) \quad \rightarrow \ 2SO_3(g)$$
$$H_2O(l) \ + \ SO_3(g) \quad \rightarrow \ H_2SO_4(l)$$

What mass of sulphuric acid should be produced?

(d) Write the equation for sodium carbonate dissolving in hydrochloric acid. If you start with 5·3 g of sodium carbonate what mass of sodium chloride will you get?

(*e*) Write an equation for the polymerisation of 10^3 moles of ethene. If you start with 28 kg of ethene what mass of poly(ethene) should you get?

35.5 Finding the formula of a substance

To find the formula you must synthesise or analyse a substance. You weigh the reagents and/or products. For example,

1 g of hydrogen and 8 g of oxygen gives 9 g of water
1 g of hydrogen **atoms** is 1 mol of hydrogen atoms
8 g of oxygen **atoms** is 0·5 mol of oxygen atoms

In water, the ratio of hydrogen atoms to oxygen atoms is 1 to 0·5. You can have 0·5 mol of atoms but you cannot have 0·5 of an atom (Dalton's atomic theory). This ratio of atoms of 1 to 0·5 must be multiplied by two so that you are dealing with whole numbers. In water there are 2 hydrogen atoms for every 1 oxygen atom: the formula of water is H_2O. You probably knew this already but the calculation above is a proof.

Sometimes you know the percentages by mass of the elements in a compound, and have to work out the formula from them. For example, red iron oxide contains 70% iron and 30% oxygen. Instead of percentages, use grams of elements. This iron oxide can be made using 70 g of iron and 30 g of oxygen:

$$70 \text{ g of iron atoms is } \frac{70}{56} = 1 \cdot 25 \text{ mol of iron atoms}$$

$$30 \text{ g of oxygen atoms is } \frac{30}{16} = 1 \cdot 875 \text{ mol of oxygen atoms}$$

In red iron oxide, the ratio of iron atoms to oxygen atoms is $1 \cdot 25 : 1 \cdot 875 = 2 : 3$. In red iron oxide there are 2 iron atoms for every 3 oxygen atoms: the formula is Fe_2O_3 and its name is iron(III) oxide.

In these calculations you may see the ratio as obviously being whole numbers, e.g. 0·25:0·50 is 1:2. The ratio of atoms must be whole numbers to obey Dalton's atomic theory. If you cannot see the ratio, divide the smallest answer you get into the other(s), e.g.

$$1.25:1.875 \text{ is the same as } 1:\frac{1.875}{1.25} = 1:1.5,$$

but you cannot have 1·5 atoms so next you double each figure which shows that 1:1·5 is the same ratio as 2:3.

These calculations give the simplest or **empirical formula** of a substance. This formula tells you the ratio of the atoms. The full answer or molecular formula might be the same or double or more than this answer. You cannot tell just from this calculation if water is H_2O or H_4O_2 or even more because in all these formulae the ratio of the atoms is the same, see Section 35.2.

Knowing the valencies of elements is a quick way of calculating the formula of a compound. It is a short cut because the formula has to be calculated as shown here.

Use the data on page 245 to do some more empirical formula calculations. (Answers on page 269.)

(*a*) copper 80%; oxygen 20%
(*b*) sodium 39·3%; chlorine 60·7%
(*c*) hydrogen 1·6%; nitrogen 22·2%; oxygen 76·2%
(*d*) sodium 32·4%; sulphur 22·5%; oxygen 45·1%
(*e*) carbon 52·2%; hydrogen 13·0%; oxygen 34·8%.

The reverse of these calculations is required sometimes. You are given the name and/or formula of a substance and asked to calculate the percentage of a particular element. For example, what is the proportion of nitrogen in ammonium nitrate? The formula is NH_4NO_3. The first step is to calculate the relative molecular mass (answer 80). There are two nitrogen atoms in one molecule of ammonium nitrate, so by mass 28/80 is nitrogen. The percentage of nitrogen is therefore 35.

35.6 Water of crystallisation

Some crystals contain water of crystallisation, see Section 32.2. To find the formula of the crystals you can do a simple experiment.

(*a*) Weigh a crucible.
(*b*) Add some hydrated crystals and reweigh.
(*c*) Heat the hydrated crystals in the crucible to drive off the water as steam.

(*d*) Let the anhydrous solid cool. Reweigh.

(*e*) Reheat the crucible and the residue to check if all the water has been driven off. Cool and reweigh. Repeat this step until the mass is constant, then you know the experiment has finished. This procedure is called 'heating to constant mass'.

You can use the relative atomic masses (Figure 35.1) to calculate the molar masses of the water and of the anhydrous solid that is left after heating. The experimental masses can be compared with the molar masses. The results of doing this experiment with hydrated magnesium sulphate crystals might be as follows:

Mass of crucible	= 15·00 g
Mass of crucible + hydrated crystals	= 18·69 g
Mass of crucible + anhydrous solid	= 16·80 g
(this was found by heating to constant mass)	

The molar mass of water, H_2O, is 18 g/mol. The formula of anhydrous magnesium sulphate is $MgSO_4$: its molar mass is $24 + 32 + (16 \times 4)$ g/mol = 120 g/mol.

In this experiment:

Mass of water	=	$(18·69 - 16·80)$ g	= 1·89 g
Mass of anhydrous substance	=	$(16·80 - 15·00)$ g	= 1·80 g
Amount of steam	=	$\dfrac{1·89}{18}$ mol	= 0·105 mol
Amount of anhydrous substance	=	$\dfrac{1·80}{120}$ mol	= 0·015 mol

In moles, the ratio of anhydrous substance to water is

$$0·015 : 0·105 \qquad = 1 : 7$$

If you did not see this ratio, divide the smaller figure into the larger as an extra step in the figures you write.

So the formula of the hydrated magnesium sulphate is $MgSO_4 \cdot 7H_2O$.

Use the following data for more calculations of the water of crystallisation in substances. Calculate the formulae of the substances. (Answers on page 269.)

(a) barium 56·1%; chlorine 29·1%; water 14·8%
(b) calcium 18·3%; chlorine 32·4%; water 49·3%
(c) sodium 16·1%; carbon 4·2%; oxygen 16·8%; water 62·9%
(d) calcium 23·3%; sulphur 18·6%; oxygen 37·2%; water 20·9%
(e) copper 25·6%; sulphur 12·8%; oxygen 25·6%; water 36·0%.

35.7 Electrolysis

When a cation reaches the cathode it gains electrons and becomes an atom, usually of a metal. An example is the electrolysis of sodium chloride in a Downs' cell, see Section 14.3.

$$Na^+ + e^- \rightarrow Na$$

If this equation is for moles of ions, electrons and atoms, instead of single particles, then

1 mol of sodium ions + 1 mol of electrons →
1 mol of sodium atoms

An electric current is measured in amperes and time is measured in seconds. A quantity of electricity (in coulombs, C) is measured by multiplying these two quantities together. You might let a large current flow for a short time or a small current for a long time: the result in electrolysis is the same. 1 mol of electrons is 96 500 C. This is the **Faraday constant**.

1 mol of sodium atoms weighing 23 g is formed when 96 500 coulombs of electricity flow in a circuit. At the same time, at the anode:

$$2Cl^- \rightarrow Cl_2 + 2e^-$$
71 g   2 × 96 500 C

So 96 500 C of electricity give 35·5 g of chlorine.

You can use ion–electron equations to calculate how much electricity is needed to produce

(a) 4 g of hydrogen by the electrolysis of water;
(b) 1·6 g of oxygen by the electrolysis of water;
(c) 64 g of copper from the electrolysis of copper(II) sulphate solution;
(d) 2·7 g of aluminium from the electrolysis of aluminium oxide;

(*e*) 40 tonnes of sodium hydroxide by the electrolysis of sodium chloride solution.

(Answers on page 269.)

36

Moles of Gases

36.1 Molar volume

A gas is not as easy to weigh as a solid or a liquid. The mass of the container is usually much greater than the mass of the gas and that makes accurate weighing very difficult. Instead, you can measure the volume of a gas and, if necessary, use its density to calculate its mass because mass = volume × density.

Gases vary a lot in their molar masses and in their densities: from hydrogen 2 g/mol and 0·09 g/l to uranium(VI) fluoride 352 g/mol and 15·8 g/l. The surprise comes when you divide the first quantity by the second.

Molar volume of hydrogen $= \dfrac{2}{0\cdot09} = 22$ l/mol

Molar volume of uranium(VI) fluoride $= \dfrac{352}{15\cdot8} = 22$ l/mol

If you do the calculations with very accurate results then the answer is 22·4 l/mol for all gases at the standard temperature (0 °C) and the standard pressure (101 kPa – kilopascals, or 1000 millibars as the weathermen say). You would not find it comfortable if the temperature was always 0 °C. Doing experiments surrounded by icy water every day is not my idea of fun either! Gases expand when they get hot so the molar volume is usually taken to be 24 l/mol at room temperature (20 °C) and standard pressure.

Long before it was known how many particles there were in 1 mol of a gas, Avogadro had stated this law (1811):

Equal volumes of all gases at the same temperature and pressure contain the same number of molecules.

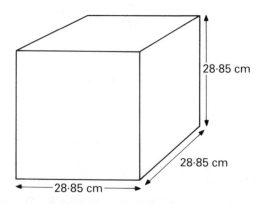

Fig. 36.1. The molar volume of any gas at 20 °C and standard pressure is 24 000 cm^3 (ml) or 24 litres

36.2 Burning gases

Many of our homes, schools and factories are heated by burning natural gas, CH_4. The equation for the reaction is:

$CH_4(g)$	+ $2O_2(g)$	$\rightarrow CO_2(g)$	+ $2H_2O(g)$
1 molecule	2 molecules	1 molecule	2 molecules

Multiplied by 6×10^{23} this gives:

1 mol	2 mol	1 mol	2 mol

Every mole of gas occupies 24 000 ml:

24 000 ml	48 000 ml	24 000 ml	48 000 ml
			(while a gas)

In a laboratory experiment you might start with 24 ml of methane, one thousandth of a mole. You would need 48 ml of oxygen to burn it. Air is only one-fifth oxygen, so you would need $48 \times 5 = 240$ ml of air.

You would probably make all your measurements at room temperature, say 20 °C. When the temperature is below 100 °C, the steam condenses to water. A liquid has a very small volume compared to its gas, so ignore it, and all you would have at the end is 24 ml of carbon dioxide.

[18 g is the mass of 1 mole of water. Water has a density of 1 g/ml. 1 mole of liquid water occupies 18 ml. One thousandth of a mole of water occupies 0·018 ml. This volume is so small you cannot measure it in a burette. It is negligible compared to 24 or 48 ml.]

When you go camping or caravanning you probably burn butane gas (C_4H_{10}) from a cylinder. The equation for the reaction is:

$$2C_4H_{10}(g) \quad +13O_2(g) \qquad \rightarrow 8CO_2(g) \qquad +10H_2O(g)$$

As before:

$2 \times 24\ 000$ ml	$13 \times 24\ 000$ ml	$8 \times 24\ 000$ ml	$10 \times 24\ 000$ ml
48 000 ml	312 000 ml	192 000 ml	240 000 ml

Notice that the butane gas takes a lot of oxygen to burn completely – and even more air. You must ventilate your tent or caravan very thoroughly to stay alive.

Now write an equation for burning octane, C_8H_{18}. A car does this. Petrol is sprayed into air in the carburettor and burnt in the cylinders of the engine to make the car go. One litre of liquid petrol weighs 700 g.

(a) What amount (in moles) of octane is there in 1 litre?
(b) What volume of octane vapour (gas) is this?
(c) What volume of oxygen is needed to burn this octane?
(d) What volume of air is needed to burn this octane?

The average car in 1985 travelled 8 km per litre of petrol.

36.3 The electrolysis of 'water'

If you electrolyse dilute sulphuric acid, dilute sodium hydroxide solution or dilute sodium sulphate solution you get the same result, see Section 14.2. You make twice as much hydrogen as oxygen. If you get 48 ml of hydrogen, you also get 24 ml of oxygen.

$$\text{amount of hydrogen } \textbf{molecules} \quad = \frac{48}{24\ 000} \text{ mol } = 0 \cdot 002 \text{ mol}$$

$$\text{amount of oxygen } \textbf{molecules} \quad = \frac{24}{24\ 000} \text{ mol } = 0 \cdot 001 \text{ mol}$$

Hydrogen and oxygen molecules both contain two atoms each. In the water that you have electrolysed there are 0.002×2 moles of hydrogen atoms for every 0.001×2 moles of oxygen atoms. The ratio of atoms is two of hydrogen to one of oxygen. The empirical formula of water is H_2O.

The Faraday constant (see Section 35.7) can be used in electrolysis calculations for gases. For example, in the electrolysis of water (see Section 14.2):

At the cathode:

$$2H^+(aq) + 2e^- \rightarrow H_2(g)$$

So for moles of particles in this equation, $2 \times 96\,500$ C of electricity with 2 moles of hydrogen ions will give 1 mole (2 g or 24 l) of hydrogen molecules.

At the anode:

$$4OH^-(aq) \rightarrow 2H_2O(l) + O_2(g) + 4e^-$$

So $4 \times 96\,500$ C of electricity flow when 1 mole (32 g or 24 l) of oxygen gas is made.

If you use $4 \times 96\,500$ C of electricity then you will get 2 moles of hydrogen (48 l) and 1 mole of oxygen (24 l): the ratio of hydrogen to oxygen by volume is 2:1.

Now you can calculate how much electricity will give you 24 l of chlorine in a Downs' cell or a membrane cell.

36.4 Gases in reactions

When you add an acid to calcium carbonate, the gas carbon dioxide escapes. To be sure the carbonate reacts completely, you probably use an excess of the acid – the quantity is not important if you are doing a calculation.

$$CaCO_3(s) + 2HCl(aq) \rightarrow CaCl_2(aq) + H_2O(l) + CO_2(g)$$

1 molecule   1 molecule

Multiplied by 6×10^{23} this is the same as saying:

1 mol   1 mol

100 g   24 l

So if you start with 1 g of calcium carbonate you would get 240 ml of carbon dioxide.

Here are some problems that you can solve in similar way. In each case you need to write the equation for the reaction before you can do any sums. (Answers on page 270.)

(a) If you put 0·24 g of magnesium into plenty of hydrochloric acid, what volume of hydrogen will you get?

(b) If you heat 8·4 g of sodium hydrogencarbonate, what volume of carbon dioxide will you get?

(c) If you put 8·4 g of sodium hydrogencarbonate into plenty of hydrochloric acid, what volume of carbon dioxide will you get?

(d) What mass of pure hydrogen peroxide is needed to make 120 ml of oxygen?

(e) If 1000 tonnes of calcium carbonate are heated in a limekiln, how much carbon dioxide escapes into the atmosphere?

37

Molar Solutions

37.1 Concentration

The concentration of a solution is the amount (in moles) of a solute in one litre of a solution.

A solution that contains one mole in one litre is sometimes called a one molar solution or a 1 M solution. There are 1000 ml (cm^3) in 1 litre (l, L or dm^3). If you have 25 ml of a solution that contains 1 mol/l of solute then you have

$$1 \times 25/1000 \text{ mol of solute.}$$

If the concentration is only 0·1 mol/l then you have

$$0 \cdot 1 \times 25/1000 \text{ mol of solute.}$$

In scientific work V is the symbol used for volume and c is the symbol for concentration. If the units of V are ml of solution and of c are mol/l then you have $Vc/1000$ mol of solute.

The mass concentration of a solution is the mass of solute in a known volume of solution. The units of mass concentration may be g/l or whatever is convenient. To change from one system of describing concentration to the other you need the molar mass:

$$\text{concentration (mol/l)} = \frac{\text{mass concentration (g/l)}}{\text{molar mass (g/mol)}}$$

For example, if a solution of sodium hydroxide contains 4 g/l, then because the molar mass is 40 g/mol the concentration of the solution is 4/40 mol/l = 0·1 mol/l.

A chemist usually uses the words 'dilute' and 'concentrated' to mean that a solution has a low or a high mass concentration of solute. The words 'weak' and 'strong' are used for the proportion of the solute that is ionised: in a weak solution only a little of the solute is ionised, see Sections 21.3 and 22.1.

37.2 Titration calculations

Titrations can be done to make salts (see Section 23.3) or to measure concentrations of solutions or to find rates of reactions.

If you titrate a solution of sodium hydroxide of known concentration with hydrochloric acid, you can find the concentration of the acid. Suppose 25 ml of 0·1 mol/l sodium hydroxide neutralises 20 ml of hydrochloric acid, then

$$\text{amount of sodium hydroxide} = \frac{25 \times 0·1}{1000} \text{ mol}$$
$$= 2·5 \times 10^{-3} \text{ mol}$$

The equation of the reaction is:

$$NaOH + HCl \rightarrow NaCl + H_2O$$

1 mol of NaOH neutralises 1 mol of HCl,
so $2·5 \times 10^{-3}$ mol NaOH neutralises $2·5 \times 10^{-3}$ mol HCl.
There is $2·5 \times 10^{-3}$ mol HCl in 20 ml acid and so there is

$2·5 \times 10^{-3} \times \frac{1000}{20}$ mol of acid in 1 l of solution

$= 0·125$ mol/l
Concentration of acid $= 0·125$ mol/l
Molar mass of HCl $= 1 + 35·5$ g/mol $= 36·5$ g/mol
So, mass concentration of hydrochloric acid $= 0·125 \times 36·5$ g/l
$= 4·56$ g/l

Calculations like this can be done to find an unknown concentration, an unknown volume of a solution or the ratio of the molecules in the equation for a reaction.

Here is a calculation for you to do: 25 ml of sodium hydrogencarbonate solution is neutralised by 20 ml of 0·125 mol/l nitric acid. Calculate (*a*) the concentration (molar) of the sodium hydrogencarbonate solution, and (*b*) its mass concentration.

38

Analysis

38.1 Look carefully

If you have been given a substance to analyse which you think or are told is an acid, base or a salt, look carefully at it. If it is a solid with one of the following colours you may have a quick start:

green	iron(II) compound
yellow or pale violet	iron(III) compound
blue	copper(II) compound

If it is white then it may be a sodium, potassium, magnesium, calcium, aluminium, zinc or ammonium compound. You must add water to a little of any solid just in case it is anhydrous: the colour of a compound may only appear when it is hydrated. Many oxides are coloured, for example manganese(IV) oxide, copper(II) oxide and iron(II) diiron(III) oxide are black, lead(IV) oxide and copper(I) oxide are brown and iron(III) oxide is red.

If the substance is crystalline it is probably soluble in water. If the substance is a powder it may have been made by precipitation or by heating some other substance.

38.2 Solubility

Does the substance dissolve in water? There is a list of the common soluble and insoluble compounds in Section 13.3.

If you are given a solution of a substance, then test it with litmus to see if it is definitely acidic or alkaline. If you cannot find a metal in it then you may have been given the acid itself. If you cannot find a non-metal in it then you have been given an alkali. Some salts in solution do not have a pH of 7 because they hydrolyse (react with water). You could be given an acid salt, see Section 23.7.

If the substance is insoluble in water you may be told to dissolve it in a dilute acid. Watch for any gas that bubbles off – the most likely one is carbon dioxide, which shows the substance is a carbonate, see Figure 21.2.

38.3 Heat the substance

Sometimes you are told to heat a substance because that will give some clues about its identity. Does it sublime – go straight from solid to gas and back to solid where the test tube is cold? If so, it may be an ammonium compound.

Does it give off carbon dioxide? Test with calcium hydroxide solution (limewater), as in Figure 21.2. This test shows the compound is a carbonate. If steam comes off as well (you see condensation where the tube is cold) then the substance is a hydrogencarbonate or a hydrated carbonate.

Does it give off brown fumes of nitrogen dioxide which are acidic? These have a strong smell and are poisonous so you may be told to do this test in a fume cupboard. Oxygen is given off at the same time so you can test the gas to see if it relights a glowing splint. These tests show the substance is a nitrate. A few nitrates (sodium and potassium) only give off oxygen.

38.4 Four reliable tests for common types of salt

(*a*) A **carbonate**: to the substance (solid or solution) add dilute hydrochloric acid. Carbon dioxide comes off. This gas turns calcium hydroxide solution milky, see Section 21.1.

(*b*) A **chloride**: to a solution of the substance add dilute nitric acid. Then add a few drops of silver nitrate (or lead(II) nitrate) solution. A white precipitate of silver or lead(II) chloride forms, see Section 23.5(c).

(*c*) A **sulphate**: to a solution of the substance add dilute hydrochloric acid. Then add some barium chloride solution. A white precipitate of barium sulphate forms, see Section 23.5(b).

(*d*) A **nitrate**: to the substance (solid or solution) add some aluminium powder (or Devarda's alloy which contains aluminium, zinc and copper). Then add some sodium hydroxide solution. Warm the mixture very carefully because the reaction when it starts may be vigorous. Don't be misled by the hydrogen that bubbles off. Test the gases for ammonia: strong smell, alkaline to damp litmus paper and forms white clouds with fumes from a drop of concentrated hydrochloric acid held on the end of a glass rod.

There is an alternative test for a nitrate: to a solution of the unknown substance add dilute sulphuric acid – there should be no fizzing. Next add iron(II) sulphate solution and cool the mixture. Finally, with great care, hold the test tube at 45° and pour in some concentrated sulphuric acid. A brown ring just above the layer of concentrated acid, which may only last a short time, will show the presence of a nitrate in the unknown substance.

38.5 A flame test

This is a quick test that sometimes gives you a useful answer. Put some dilute hydrochloric acid on a watch glass or in a test tube. Take a piece of nichrome wire (the sort used for toasters, electric fires and irons) and moisten it with the acid. Hold the wire in the outer flame of a Bunsen burner which has the airhole open. When the wire is clean it will give no colour to the flame. Then dip the wire in the acid and touch some of the solid substance or solution. It will stick by surface tension. Hold the wire in the flame again. If you get a colour then you know the substance is a metallic compound:

persistent, bright orange-yellow	sodium compound
pale violet (lilac)	potassium compound
orange-red	calcium compound
green with blue centre	copper compound

This is a heating and cooling test which depends on the movement of electrons in ions. It is not a combustion.

38.6 Alkali tests

Solutions of many metallic salts will give precipitates with sodium hydroxide solution and/or ammonia solution (aqueous ammonia, ammonium hydroxide), see Section 22.2(f) and Figure 22.1.

If you are told to warm a substance carefully (solid or solution) with sodium hydroxide solution or with calcium hydroxide, then be prepared to test for ammonia, see Sections 22.2(g) and 38.4(d). This will show whether the substance is an ammonium compound.

When you have finished all the tests on an unknown substance and recorded all your observations and deductions (inferences), look at them carefully. Use your common sense and draw a logical conclusion from your results.

38.7 A final warning

If you have a home chemistry set, be careful to follow the instructions for experiments. Many substances are poisonous. Many substances are not safe to mix at random with others. Even fully trained chemists sometimes have accidents. If you see the following signs be particularly careful:

EXPLOSIVE

OXIDISING
(agent)

CORROSIVE

HIGHLY
FLAMMABLE
(burns
readily)

HARMFUL
or IRRITANT

TOXIC

When travelling you can look at the labels on road tankers to see what they are carrying. There is a Hazchem code which states what must be done if there is a fire or spillage and a telephone number for specialist advice.

ANSWERS TO QUESTIONS

7.9   (*a*)   Paint would chip, exposing the iron; hence rusting occurs.

      (*b*)   Luigi Galvani (1737–98, Italy) noticed frogs' legs twitch if in contact with two metals. This showed that nerve messages are electrical.

8.2   (*a*), (*c*) and (*d*) are physical changes

8.3   (*a*), (*c*) and (*d*) are chemical changes

9.3   Ring forms nearest hydrochloric acid, hence ammonia travels faster. Regain water from squash by distillation. Collect perfume by adsorption on charcoal.

10.2   Iodine with starch gives a blue-black coloration.

12.11   One-tenth of an iceberg is seen above the surface of water.

12.15   (*a*)   Dissolve sodium chloride in water. Filter off silicon dioxide. Evaporate filtrate to regain sodium chloride.

      (*b*)   Paper chromatography using solution obtained by mashing grass in propanone.

      (*c*)   Use magnet to attract iron.

      (*d*)   Distillation leaves solid calcium sulphate.

      (*e*)   Sublimation of ammonium chloride.

      (*f*)   Absorb carbon dioxide in sodium hydroxide solution. Add hydrochloric acid to the solution to regain carbon dioxide.

      (*g*)   Cork floats on water.

      (*h*)   Absorb ammonia in hydrochloric acid. Warm solution with sodium hydroxide to regain ammonia.

      (*i*)   Paper chromatography.

      (*j*)   Add water, boil, sodium chloride crystallises first.

      (*k*)   Dissolve copper in moderately concentrated nitric acid. Copper regained at cathode upon electrolysis.

      (*l*)   Dissolve sodium chloride in water. Filter off calcium carbonate. Evaporate filtrate to regain sodium chloride.

14.2   Hydrogen in right hand tube in figure; twice the volume of oxygen.

14.6   Between inert graphite electrodes copper(II) chloride solution would give copper and chlorine, and molten lead(II) bromide would give lead and bromine.

17.9 Hydrogen as fuel, see Section 5.5: sun (*d*).

24.3 Milk of Magnesia, see Section 22.4(a).

24.4 Black solid becomes red solid. Do not heat the copper(II) oxide until any air in the apparatus has been displaced by ammonia.

26.3 Burning paper: cut off air, pour water on.

Burning fat: cut off air.

Burning gas: turn off.

30.3 20 protons in calcium atom and ion.

32.5 A a covalent macromolecular substance (carbon as diamond)

B an ionic compound (sodium chloride)

C a metal (iron)

D a simple molecular substance (sulphur in its rhombic form)

E a simple molecular substance (ice)

F a simple molecular substance which partially ionises in water (pure ethanoic acid)

G a simple molecular substance which partially ionises in water (ammonia).

33.3 See Section 35.4.

34.1 Car windscreen: transparent

Kitchen tile: opaque

Frosted glass: translucent.

(*a*) $NaOH(aq) + HCl(aq) \rightarrow NaCl(aq) + H_2O(l)$

(*b*) $CaCO_3(s) \rightarrow CaO(s) + CO_2(g)$

(*c*) $2H_2O_2(aq) \rightarrow 2H_2O(l) + O_2(g)$

(*d*) $2NaHCO_3(s) \rightarrow Na_2CO_3(s) + H_2O(l) + CO_2(g)$

(*e*) $NH_4Cl(s \text{ or } aq) + NaOH(aq) \rightarrow NaCl(aq) + H_2O(l) + NH_3(g)$

No coloured substances.

34.2 (*a*) $NaOH(aq) + HNO_3(aq) \rightarrow NaNO_3(aq) + H_2O(l)$

(*b*) $Ca(OH)_2(s \text{ or } aq) + CO_2(g) \rightarrow CaCO_3(s) + H_2O(l)$

(*c*) $NaHCO_3 (s \text{ or } aq) + HCl(aq) \rightarrow NaCl(aq) + H_2O(l) + CO_2(g)$

(*d*) $AgNO_3(aq) + KCl(aq) \rightarrow AgCl(s) + KNO_3(aq)$

(*e*) $BaCl_2(aq) + MgSO_4(aq) \rightarrow BaSO_4(s) + MgCl_2(aq)$

34.3 (*a*) $2NaOH(aq) + H_2SO_4(aq) \rightarrow Na_2SO_4(aq) + 2H_2O(l)$

(b) $Na_2CO_3(s \text{ or } aq) + 2HNO_3(aq) \rightarrow 2NaNO_3(aq) + H_2O(l) + CO_2(g)$

(c) $Fe_3O_4(s) + 4CO(g) \rightarrow 3Fe(s) + 4CO_2(g)$

(d) $4CuO(s) + CH_4(g) \rightarrow 4Cu(s) + CO_2(g) + 2H_2O(l)$

(e) $2Mg(s) + O_2(g) \rightarrow 2MgO(s)$

35.4 (a) $CaCO_3(s) \quad \rightarrow CaO(s) \quad + CO_2(g)$

$M = 100\,g/mol \quad M = 56\,g/mol \quad M = 44\,g/mol$

$10\,g = 0.1\,mol \quad 0.1\,mol = 5.6\,g \quad 0.1\,mol = 4.4\,g$

(b) $KOH(aq) \quad + HNO_3(aq) \rightarrow KNO_3(aq) \quad + H_2O$

$M = 56\,g/mol$

$2.8\,g = 0.05\,mol \quad 0.05\,mol \qquad 0.05\,mol \qquad\qquad 0.05\,mol$

$\qquad\qquad\qquad\qquad\qquad\qquad\quad M = 101\,g/mol$

$\qquad\qquad\qquad\qquad\qquad\qquad\quad 0.05\,mol = 5.05\,g$

(c) 32 g of sulphur will make 98 g of H_2SO_4

So, 32 tonnes of sulphur will make 98 tonnes of H_2SO_4

(d) $Na_2CO_3(s) + 2HCl(aq) \rightarrow 2NaCl(aq) + H_2O(l) + CO_2(g)$

$M = 106\,g/mol$

$5.3\,g = 0.05\,mol \qquad\qquad M = 58.5\,g/mol$

$\qquad\qquad\qquad\qquad\qquad 2\,mol = 117\,g$

$\qquad\qquad\qquad\qquad\qquad 0.1\,mol = 5.85\,g$

(e) $10^3C_2H_4(g) \qquad\qquad \rightarrow (C_2H_4)_{1000}(s)$

$M = 28\,g/mol \qquad\qquad M = 28 \times 10^3\,g/mol$

$10^3\,mol = 28 \times 10^3\,g \quad 1\,mol = 28 \times 10^3\,g$

$28\,kg \qquad\qquad\qquad\quad 28\,kg$

35.5 (a) CuO (b) NaCl (c) HNO_3 (d) Na_2SO_4

(e) C_2H_6O (ethanol)

35.6 (a) $BaCl_2 \cdot 2H_2O$ (b) $CaCl_2 \cdot 6H_2O$ (c) $Na_2CO_3 \cdot 10H_2O$

(d) $CaSO_4 \cdot 2H_2O$ (e) $CuSO_4 \cdot 5H_2O$

35.7 (a) $4H^+ + 4e^- \qquad\qquad\qquad \rightarrow 2H_2$

$\qquad\quad 4 \times 96500\,C$

$\qquad\qquad = 386000\,C$

(b) $4OH^- \rightarrow 4e^- \qquad\qquad\quad + 2H_2O + O_2$

$\qquad\quad 4 \times 96\,500\,C \qquad\qquad\qquad 32\,g$

$\qquad\qquad\qquad\qquad\qquad\qquad\qquad 1.6\,g$

Therefore the amount of electricity required is:

$$\frac{1.6 \times 4 \times 96\,500\,C}{32}$$

$$= 19300\,C$$

(c) $Cu^{2+} + 2e^- \rightarrow Cu$
$\quad\quad 2 \times 96500\,C \quad 64\,g$

(d) $Al^{3+} + 3e^- \rightarrow Al$
$\quad\quad 3 \times 96500\,C \quad M = 27\,g/mol$
$\quad\quad 3 \times 9650\,C \quad 2.7\,g$

Therefore the amount of electricity required is:

$$\frac{2.7 \times 3 \times 96500\,C}{27} = 3 \times 9650\,C$$
$$= 28950\,C$$

(e) $2NaCl + 2H_2O \rightarrow 2NaOH + H_2 + Cl_2$
$\quad\quad\quad\quad\quad\quad\quad M = 40\,g/mol$
$\quad\quad\quad\quad\quad\quad\quad 2\,mol \quad\quad 1\,mol$
$\quad\quad\quad\quad\quad\quad\quad$ so $80\,g$ here

$2H^+ + 2e^- \rightarrow H_2$
$\quad\quad 2 \times 96500\,C \quad 1\,mol$
$\quad\quad$ (or as in 36.3 below)

$80\,g$ NaOH with $1\,mol\ H_2$ by $2 \times 96500\,C$

40 tonnes NaOH by $\dfrac{40 \times 10^6 \times 2 \times 96500\,C}{80}$

$$= 9.65 \times 10^{10}\,C$$

36.2   (a) $M(C_8H_{18}) = 114\,g/mol$

1 litre weighs $700\,g = \dfrac{700}{114}\,mol$

$$= 6.14\,mol$$

(b) $\dfrac{700}{114} \times 24\,litres$

$$= 147.37\,litres$$

(c) $C_8H_{18} + 12.5O_2 \rightarrow 8CO_2 + 9H_2O$
$\quad\quad 1\,mol \quad\quad 12.5\,mol$

Volume of O_2 here $= \dfrac{700 \times 24 \times 12.5}{114}\,litres$

$$= 1842.11\,litres$$

(d)   Volume of air here $= \dfrac{700 \times 24 \times 12.5 \times 5}{114}\,litres$

$$= 9210.53\,litres$$

36.3 $2Cl^- \rightarrow Cl_2 + 2e^-$
$\quad\quad\quad\quad 71\,g$
$\quad\quad\quad\quad$ or $24\,litres \quad 2 \times 96500\,C$

36.4   (a) $Mg + 2HCl \rightarrow MgCl_2 + H_2$

24 g   24 litres

0.24 g   0.24 litres

    (b) $2NaHCO_3 \rightarrow Na_2CO_3 + H_2O + CO_2$

2×84 g   24 litres

8.4 g $\dfrac{8.4 \times 24 \text{ litres}}{2 \times 84}$

                                   = 1.2 litres

    (c) $NaHCO_3 + HCl \rightarrow NaCl + H_2O + CO_2$

84 g   24 litres

8.4 g   2.4 litres

    (d) $2H_2O_2 \rightarrow 2H_2O + O_2$

2×34 g   24 litres

                         = 24 000 ml

                         = 120 ml

                         = 0.24 litres

$\dfrac{2 \times 34 \times 120 \text{ g}}{24\,000}$

     = 0.34 g

    (e) $CaCO_3 \rightarrow CaO + CO_2$

100 g   24 litres

1000 tonnes 240×10^6 litres

                       = 240 000 m³

37.2   (a) $NaHCO_3 + HNO_3 \rightarrow NaNO_3 + H_2O + CO_2$

Amount of nitric acid = $\dfrac{20 \times 0.125 \text{ mol}}{1000}$

                          = 2.5×10^{-3} mol

1 mol of HNO_3 neutralises 1 mol of $NaHCO_3$

So 2.5×10^{-3} mol neutralises 2.5×10^{-3} mol $NaHCO_3$.

There is 2.5×10^{-3} mol $NaHCO_3$ in 25 ml of solution.

So there is $\dfrac{2.5 \times 10^{-3} \times 1000 \text{ mol}}{25}$ $NaHCO_3$ in 1 litre

                = 0.1 mol/litre

    (b)   Concentration of $NaHCO_3$ solution = 0.1 mol/litre

Molar mass of $NaHCO_3$ = 84 g/mol

So mass concentration   = 0.1×84 g/litre

                                 = 8.4 g/litre

Index